MULTILINGUAL VOCABULARY OF SOIL SCIENCE

VOCABULAIRE MULTILINGUE DE LA SCIENCE DU SOL

VOCABULARIO MULTILINGÜE DE LA CIENCIA DEL SUELO

The author of this vocabulary is Consultant
on Soil Problems to the Land and Water Use
Branch of the Agriculture Division.

L'auteur de ce Vocabulaire est Consultant
pour les questions de sols à la Sous-division
de l'utilisation des terres et des eaux de
la Division de l'agriculture.

El autor de este Vocabulario es Consultor de
Suelos, del Departamento de Aprovechamiento
de Tierras y Aguas, Dirección de Agricultura.

Multilingual Vocabulary of Soil Science
Vocabulaire multilingue de la science du sol
Vocabulario multilingüe de la ciencia del suelo

G. V. JACKS

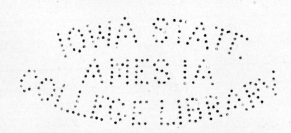
Agriculture Division
Division de l'Agriculture
Direccion de Agricultura

FOOD AND AGRICULTURE ORGANIZATION OF THE UNITED NATIONS
ORGANISATION DES NATIONS UNIES POUR L'ALIMENTATION ET L'AGRICULTURE
ORGANIZACION DE LA NACIONES UNIDAS PARA LA AGRICULTURA Y LA ALIMENTACION

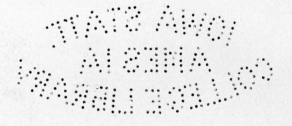

Printed in Italy

CONTENTS

TABLE DES MATIERES

Page

INDICE

PREFACE

This publication is one of the series of FAO documents designed to meet the needs of agricultural workers in the various countries of the world. The project was suggested to FAO as a result of the apparent difficulties in translating the concepts of soil terms used in one language into other languages. It is hoped that the publication of this work will assist in the international exchange of information on soils, and will lead to a greater correlation and uniformity of soil descriptions.

The initial work of collecting the terms of this glossary and getting them translated into seven other languages was begun by Dr. H. Greene in 1949. A report on the glossary was presented to the Fourth International Congress of Soil Science in Amsterdam in 1950 (Transactions, Vol.IV, pp.180-186).

As a result of this report, national nomenclature committees and individuals in many countries submitted their comments on, and corrections of, the draft glossary presented to the Amsterdam Congress.

A large number of alterations were submitted, and with the help of the suggestions received a revised draft was prepared and circulated to collaborators who made further emendations, and suggested additional terms which were incorporated in the glossary. It was apparent that it would be impossible to retain the original idea of having a single uniform definition of each term in all languages. There are many terms which are used in different senses in different languages. Thus at least three distinct meanings are given to the universally used term humus. Many terms have not exact equivalents in all languages, e.g. the German term anmooriger Boden, for which approximate equivalents in other languages have been given. Some English terms are used differently in the United Kingdom and the United States. The definitions are then distinguished by the letters (U.K.) and (U.S.) respectively.

Arrangement of the glossary

The terms have been grouped according to subject, each group being designated by a capital letter according to the following scheme:

A	Physics, general	L	Soil classification, general
B	Texture and structure	M	Organic and peat soils
C	Soil water	N	Podzolic soils
D	Chemistry	O	Gley and meadow soils
E	Organic matter, humus	P	Arid and semi-arid soils
F	Biology, ecology	Q	Saline and alkali soils
G	Cultivation, manuring, fertility	R	Tropical and sub-tropical soils
H	Soil formation, morphology	S	Intrazonal and azonal soils
I	Profile characters, horizons	T	Terracing, damming, drainage
J	Geology, topography, climate	U	Irrigation
K	Mineralogy, clay minerals	V	Erosion

Within each group the terms are numbered serially, e.g. A.1 <u>apparent density</u>, A.2 <u>cohesion</u>, and so on. Each term in the glossary is followed by its definition in the same language. The eight languages are indicated, in the order in which they occur, by the following abbreviations:-

(1)	English	Eng.		(5)	Portuguese	P.
(2)	French	F.		(6)	Italian	I.
(3)	German	D.		(7)	Dutch	Nl.
(4)	Spanish	Esp.		(8)	Swedish	S.

To locate a term in the glossary, reference should be made to one of the eight alphabetical indexes given at the end of the glossary.

Acknowledgments

The help, advice and criticism of all who have assisted in the preparation of this glossary is gratefully acknowledged, and particularly J.K. Ableiter, R. Bach, M. Baldwin, P. Boischot, C.H. Edelman, S.B. Hendricks, A. Jacob, C.E. Kellogg,

K.O. Köhler, C.A. Orvedal, M.A.R. Reicart, R.P.H. van der Schans, and R.W. Simonson, who were of great assistance to Dr. Greene in the earlier stages of preparation, and the National Nomenclature Committees, including H. Greene and A. Muir (U.K.), M.L. Jackson and members of the U.S. Nomenclature Committee (U.S.), R. Chaminade, S. Hénin and G. Aubert (France), F. Scheffer and collaborators (Germany), L.J. Medina (Venezuela) and F. Silva (Colombia), D.L. Bramão, F.C. de Freitas and collaborators (Portugal), A. Alfani (Italy), A.J. Wiggers and collaborators (Holland) and G. Torstensson and collaborators (Sweden), who gave much valuable assistance to Mr. Jacks in the later stages of preparation.

AVANT-PROPOS

Le présent ouvrage fait partie d'une série de publications de la FAO destinées à aider les spécialistes des questions agricoles dans le monde entier. Il a été préparé en raison des difficultés qui s'attachent à la traduction des termes de science du sol, et devrait donc faciliter l'échange international de renseignements sur les sols ainsi que permettre de coordonner et d'uniformiser les descriptions de sols.

C'est en 1949 que M. Greene commença à rassembler des termes de science du sol et à les faire traduire en sept langues. Cette première version du vocabulaire a fait l'objet d'un rapport au quatrième Congrès international de science du sol d'Amsterdam, en 1950 (Actes du Congrès, volume IV, pages 180-186).

A la suite de la publication de ce rapport, des comités nationaux de nomenclature et des particuliers de nombreux pays soumirent des observations et des projets de corrections concernant le texte présenté à Amsterdam.

Un nombre considérable de modifications furent proposées, et compte tenu de ces suggestions, une version revue fut envoyée aux collaborateurs, provoquant de nouvelles propositions de corrections et d'additions, qui ont été incorporées à l'ouvrage. Il est apparu qu'il serait impossible de donner de chaque terme une définition uniforme dans toutes les langues, comme il était prévu à l'origine car il n'est pas rare qu'un même terme recouvre des concepts différents d'une langue à l'autre. C'est ainsi qu'il existe au moins trois acceptions différentes pour un terme aussi universellement usité que le mot humus. De nombreux termes n'ont pas d'équivalent exact dans toutes les autres langues: l'allemand anmooriger Boden, par exemple, a fait l'objet de traductions approchées. En anglais, certains mots n'ont pas le même sens au Royaume-Uni et aux Etats-Unis, auquel cas les définitions sont précisées par (U.K.) ou (U.S.).

Organisation de l'ouvrage

Les termes sont groupés par sujets, désignés chacun par une majuscule, comme suit :

A Physique, généralités

B Texture et structure

C Eau du sol

D Chimie

E Matières organiques, humus

F Biologie, écologie

G Culture, fumure, fertilité

H Formation des sols, morphologie

I Profils, horizons

J Géologie, topographie, climat

K Minéralogie, minéraux argileux

L Classification des sols, généralités

M Sols organiques et sols tourbeux

N Sols podzoliques

O Sols de gley et sols de prairies

P Sols arides et semi-arides

Q Sols salins et alcalins

R Sols tropicaux et sub-tropicaux

S Sols intrazonaux et azonaux

T Terrasses, barrages, drainage

U Irrigation

V Erosion

Dans chaque groupe, les termes sont numérotés (par exemple A.1 densité apparente, A.2 cohésion, etc.) et suivis chacun de sa définition dans la langue considérée. Les huit langues sont indiquées dans l'ordre par les abréviations ci-après :

(1)	Anglais	Eng.	(5)	Portugais	P.
(2)	Français	F.	(6)	Italien	I.
(3)	Allemand	D	(7)	Hollandais	Nl.
(4)	Espagnol	Esp.	(8)	Suédois	S.

A la fin de l'ouvrage, huit index alphabétiques permettent de repérer le terme recherché.

Remerciements

Nous tenons à remercier tous ceux qui nous ont apporté leur aide, leurs conseils et leurs critiques lors de la préparation du vocabulaire; nous remercions en particulier MM. J. K. Ableiter, R. Bach, M. Baldwin, P. Boischot, C. H. Edelman, S. B. Hendricks, A. Jacob, C. E. Kellogg, K. O. Kohler, C. A. Ovedal, M.A.R. Reichart, R.P.H. van der Schans et R. W. Simonson qui, dans les premiers stades de la préparation, ont fourni à M. Greene une aide précieuse; les comités nationaux de nomenclature, notamment MM. H. Greene et A. Muir (R.U.), M. L. Jackson et les membres du Comité américain de nomenclature (Etats-Unis), R. Chaminade, S. Hénin et G. Aubert (France),

F. Scheffer et ses collaborateurs (Allemagne), L. J. Medina (Venezuela) et F. Silva (Colombie), D. L. Bramão, F. C. de Freitas et leurs collaborateurs (Portugal), A. Alfani (Italie), A. J. Wiggers et leurs collaborateurs (Hollande) et G. Torstensson et ses collaborateurs (Suède), qui ont grandement aidé M. Jacks à mettre la dernière main à cet ouvrage.

PREFACIO

Este vocabulario forma parte de la serie de documentos
editados por la FAO para facilitar los trabajos profesionales de
agronomía en los diversos países del mundo. El proyecto fué pro-
puesto a la Organización con motivo de las ostensibles dificulta-
des con que se tropieza al traducir de una lengua a otra el significado de los términos relativos al suelo. Se espera que me-
diante la publicación de la presente terminología se fomentará el
intercambio internacional de conocimientos edafológicos, coadyu-
vando a establecer mejores correlaciones entre los diferentes suelos y mayor uniformidad en las descripciones de los mismos.

La labor inicial de recopilación de los vocablos en in-
glés y de conseguir su traducción a otras siete lenguas fué aco-
metida por el Dr. H. Greene en 1949. El glosario, con un informe
anexo, se presentó al Cuarto Congreso Internacional de Ciencias
del Suelo, celebrado en Amsterdam en 1950 (Actas, Vol. IV, págs.
180-186).

En virtud del mencionado informe, los comités nacionales
de nomenclatura e individuos particulares de muchos países hicie-
ron observaciones y recomendaron correcciones al glosario provisional enviado al susodicho Congreso.

Las modificaciones indicadas fueron copiosas, e incor-
porando los cambios propuestos se preparó un glosario provisional
revisado que se hizo distribuir entre los colaboradores, quienes
introdujeron otras enmiendas y sugirieron además nuevos vocablos
que han quedado incluídos. Se puso en evidencia que sería impo-
sible apegarse a la idea original de establecer definiciones úni-
cas uniformes de cada término, válidas para todas las lenguas, ya
que el significado de muchos de ellos variaba en los distintos
idiomas. Así resulta que la palabra humus, universalmente usada,
aparece con no menos de tres disímiles connotaciones. Muchas ex-
presiones no tienen equivalencia exacta en las diversas lenguas;
por ejemplo: la alemana anmooriger Boden, para la cual se han
introducido equivalentes aproximados en otros idiomas. Algunos
términos ingleses no se emplean con igual significación en el
Reino Unido que en los Estados Unidos. Las definiciones se dis-
tinguen entonces con las respectivas notaciones (U.K.) y (U.S.).

Disposición del glosario

Las voces se han agrupado de acuerdo con la materia a que
se refieren, designando cada grupo por una letra mayúscula, confor-
me a la siguiente distribución:

A	Física general	L	Clasificación general de suelos
B	Textura y estructura	M	Suelos orgánicos y turbosos
C	Aguas freáticas	N	Suelos rodsólicos
D	Química	O	Suelos de gley y de pradera
E	Materia orgánica, humus	P	Suelos áridos y semiáridos
F	Biología, ecología	Q	Suelos salinos y alcalinos
G	Cultivo, abono orgánico, fertilidad	R	Suelos tropicales y subtropicales
H	Formación del suelo, morfología	S	Suelos intrazonales y azonales
I	Caracteres del perfil, horizontes	T	Terraplenes, presas, avenamiento
J	Geología, topografía, clima	U	Riego
K	Minerología, minerales arcillosos	V	Erosión

Dentro de cada grupo se han dispuesto los términos en
series, ejemplo A.1 = densidad aparente, A.2 = cohesión, y así
sucesivamente. A cada vocablo le sigue su definición en el idio-
ma correspondiente, que en número de ocho se han colocado en el
orden que sigue, indicados por medio de abreviaturas:

(1)	Inglés	Eng.		(5)	Portugués	P.
(2)	Francés	F.		(6)	Italiano	I.
(3)	Alemán	D.		(7)	Holandés	Nl.
(4)	Español	Esp.		(8)	Sueco	S.

Para encontrar un término en el glosario, deberá consul-
tarse uno de los ocho índices alfabéticos que figuran al final.

Agradecimientos

Se agradecen la ayuda, el consejo y las críticas cons-
tructivas de todos aquellos que han colaborado en la preparación
de este glosario, en particular a los señores J. K. Ableiter,
R. Bach, M. Baldwin, P. Boischot, C. H. Edelman, S. B. Hendricks,
A. Jacob, C. E. Kellog, K. O. Kohler, C. A. Ovedal, M.A.R. Reichart,

R.F.H. van der Schans y R. W. Simonson, quienes prestaron valiosa
ayuda al Dr. Greene en las primeras etapas del trabajo; a los Comités Nacionales de Nomenclatura, en que tomaron parte H. Greene
y A. Muir (R.U.), M. L. Jackson y demás miembros del Comité de Nomenclatura de los Estados Unidos; a R. Chaminade, S. Hénin y G. Aubert (Francia), F. Scheffer y sus colaboradores (Alemania), L. J.
Medina (Venezuela) y F. Silva (Colombia), D. L. Bramão, F. de Freitas y sus colaboradores (Portugal), A. Alfani (Italia), A. J. Wiggers y sus colaboradores (Holanda) y G. Torstensson y sus colaboradores (Suecia), por tan estimable cooperación con el señor Jacks en
las últimas etapas de preparación.

Section A

PHYSICS, GENERAL

PHYSIQUE, GENERALITES

FISICA, GENERAL

Eng.   <u>apparent density</u>
       <u>bulk density</u>
           Mass of dry soil per unit volume.

F.   <u>densité apparente</u>
           Masse de l'unité de volume apparent du sol.

D.   <u>scheinbare Dichte</u> (f)
           Masse des trockenen Bodens pro Volumeinheit.

Esp.   <u>densidad aparente</u>
           Densidad de un cuerpo incluyendo los espacios
           porosos.

P.   <u>densidade aparente</u>
           A densidade de um corpo incluindo os espaços
           interstíciais.

I.   <u>densità</u> (f) <u>apparente</u>
           Densità di un corpo che comprende piccoli vani
           e cavità inclusi.

Nl.   <u>schijnbare dichtheid</u>
           Soortelijk gewicht van een denkbeeldig massief
           lichaam, even zwaar en begrensd door hetzelfde
           buitenoppervlak als het beschouwde poreuze.

S.   <u>volymvikt</u>
           Vikten av volymsenheten i ostörd (eller i vissa
           fall störd) lagring.

Eng. conesion
       The property of particles sticking together to form an
       aggregate.

F.   cohésion
       Propriété permettant aux particules de sol de rester
       associées les unes aux autres.

D.   Kohäsion (f)
       Zusammenhaften von Einzelteilen zu einer grösseren
       Masse.

Esp. cohesión
       Propiedad que tienen las partículas de pegarse entre
       si para formar agregados.

P.   coesão
       Propriedade das partículas se ligarem entre si formando
       agregados.

I.   coesione (f)
       La proprietà di rimanere attaccati insieme e formare
       una massa più grande.

Nl.   cohaesie
       De eigenschap van het samenkleven.

S.   kohesion
      sammanhållning
       Egenskapen att häfta samman och bilda en större massa.

Eng. consistence
       The degree of cohesion of soil or of soil aggregates;
       resistance to deformation; feel to the fingers.

F.   consistance
       Exprime la nature du comportement du sol au **cours de**
       sa manipulation. (S'emploie généralement avec un
       adjectif.)

D.   Konsistenz
       Art des Zusammenhaltens des Bodens oder der Aggregate.

Esp. consistencia
       El grado de cohesión de la masa del suelo o de los
       agregados del suelo.

P.   consistência
       Grau de coesão da massa do solo ou dos agregados.

I.   consistenza (f)
       Il grado di coesione della massa del terreno o degli
       aggregati del terreno.

Nl.   consistentie
       De mate van samenhangen van de grondmassa of van grond-
       aggregaten.

S.   konsistens
       Graden av jordmassans eller jordaggregatens samman-
       hållning.

Eng. <u>plastic</u>
Capable of undergoing deformation without rupture.

F. <u>plastique</u>
Se déformant sans rupture.

D. <u>plastisch</u>
Verformung ohne Bruch ertragend.

Esp. <u>plástico</u>
·Que se deforma sin romperse.

P. <u>plástico</u>
Capaz de se deformar sem quebrar.

I. <u>plastico</u>
Che sopporta una deformazione senza rompersi.

Nl. <u>plastisch</u>
Laat vervorming toe zonder te scheuren.

S. <u>plastisk</u>
Formbar.

Eng. <u>permeability</u>
>   Readiness with which air or water can pass through
>   soil.

F.   <u>perméabilité</u>
>   Facilité suivant laquelle le sol se laisse traverser
>   par l'eau.

D.   <u>Durchlässigkeit</u> (f)
>   Fähigkeit des Bodens, Gase oder Flüssigkeiten hindurch-
>   zulassen.

Esp. <u>permeabilidad</u>
>   Facilidad con que el aire o el agua puede pasar a
>   través del suelo.

P.   <u>permeabilidade</u>
>   Facilidade com que o solo se deixa atravessar pela água
>   ou pelo ar.

I.   <u>permeabilità</u> (f)
>   Speditezza con cui l'aria e l'acqua possono attraver-
>   sare il terreno.

Nl.   <u>doorlatend vermogen</u>
>   Gemak waarmee lucht of water zich door de grond kunnen
>   bewegen.

S.   <u>genomsläpplighet</u>
>   Jordens förmåga att släppa igenom luft eller vatten.

A6

Eng. <u>porosity</u>
<u>pore space</u>
Fraction of the total soil volume not occupied by solid
particles.

F. <u>porosité</u>
(1) volume des espaces lacunaires par rapport au volume
total apparent du sol.
(2) qualitativement: présence d'espaces lacunaires.

D. <u>Porosität</u>
Art und Umfang der Porenverteilung im Boden.

Esp. <u>porosidad del suelo</u>
Grado de presencia de poros en el suelo.

P. <u>porosidade</u>
Volume total do espaço intersticial do solo.

I. <u>porosità</u> (f)
Proporzione di pori contenuti nel terreno.

Nl. <u>porositeit</u>
Graad waarin de grond poriën bevat.

S. <u>luckringsgrad</u>
Graden av porutrymme i jorden.

Eng. capillary porosity
       Volume of small pores in soil that hold water by capil-
       larity.

F.   porosité capillaire
       Volume des petits espaces lacunaires du sol retenant
       l'eau par capillarité.

D.   kapillares Hohlraumvolumen
       Volumen der kleinen Hohlräume im Boden, die das Wasser
       kapillarisch festhalten.

Esp. espacio poroso capilar
       Suma de los volúmenes de los poros pequeños que retie↑
       el agua por capilaridad.

P.   porosidade capilar
       Volume dos poros pequenos do solo que retêm água por
       capilaridade.

I.   porosità capillare
       Volume di pori piccoli nel terreno che trattiene l'a
       per capillarità.

Nl.   volume der capillaire ruimten
       Volume der gezamenlijke kleinere bodemruimten, ↑ie
       bepaalde omstandigheden door toedoen van capillair↑
       krachten met water gevuld blijven.

S.   kapillär porvolym
       Volymen av porer i jorden, som förmå kvarhålla vat
       hjälp av kapillärkraften.

Eng.   <u>non-capillary porosity</u>
Volume of large pores in soil that do not hold water by
capillarity.

F.   <u>porosité non capillaire</u>
Volume des grands espaces lacunaires du sol ne retenant
pas l'eau par capillarité.

D.   <u>spannungsfreies (nichtkapillares) Hohlraumvolumen</u>
Volumen der grossen Hohlräume im Boden, die kein Wasser
kapillarisch festhalten.

Esp.   <u>espaćio poroso no capilar</u>
Suma de los volumenes de los poros grandes que no
retienen el agua por capilaridad.

P.   <u>porosidade não capilar</u>
Volume dos poros grande do solo que não retêm água por
capilaridade.

I.   <u>porosità non capillare</u>
Volume di larghi pori nel terreno che non trattiene
l'acqua per capillarità.

Nl.   <u>volume der niet-capillaire ruimten</u>
Volume der gezamenlijke grotere bodemruimten, die door
capillaire krachten onder bepaalde omstandigheden niet
met water gevuld blijven.

S.   <u>icke-kapillär porvolym</u>
Volymen av porer i jorden, som icke förmå kvarhålla
vatten med hjälp av kapillärkraften.

Eng.   residual shrinkage
>   A decrease in volume smaller than that of water lost
>   at the same time (U.K.).
>   The decrease in volume after the proportionality
>   between water loss and volume change ceases (U.S.).

F.   retrait résiduel
>   Diminution de volume du sol plus petite que celui de
>   l'eau perdue dans le même temps.

D.   Restschrumpfung (f)
>   Volumenverminderung, die kleiner ist als der gleich-
>   zeitige Wasserverlust.

Esp.   contracción residual
>   Una disminución en volumen menor que la del agua per-
>   dida en ese tiempo.

P.   contracção residual
>   Decréscimo de volume menor do que o da perda da água
>   no mesmo tempo.

I.   ritiro (m) residuo
>   contrazione (f) residua
>   Una diminuzione in volume minore di quella dovuta
>   all'acqua perduta nello stesso tempo.

Nl.   krimprest
>   Volumevermindering, die bij drogen van een grond nog
>   plaats vindt, nadat het gebied, waarin krimp en vocht-
>   verlies evenredig zijn, is gepasseerd.

S.   restkrympning
>   En volymminskning som är mindre än den som förorsakas
>   av vattenförlusten under samma tid.

Section B

TEXTURE AND STRUCTURE

TEXTURE ET STRUCTURE

TEXTURA Y ESTRUCTURA

Eng. <u>texture</u>
        Composition of soil in respect to particle size (U.K.).
        Classification of soil based on the relative amounts of
        the various size groups of individual soil grains (U.S.)

F. <u>texture</u>
        Composition du sol résultant de la dimension de ses
        particules.

D. <u>Textur</u> (f)
        Zusammensetzung des Bodens in Bezug auf die Teilchen-
        grösse.

Esp. <u>textura</u>
        Composición del suelo en relación con la dimensión de
        las partículas.

P. <u>textura</u>
        Composição do solo em relação ao tamanho das partículas.

I. <u>intessitura</u> (f)
        Composizione del terreno riguardo alle dimensioni delle
        particelle.

Nl. <u>granulaire samenstelling</u>
        De samenstelling van de grond met betrekking tot zijn
        korrelgrootte.

S. <u>textur</u>
        Jordens sammansättning med avseende på partikelstorlek.

B2

Eng. gravel
   Particles between 20 and 2 mm in diameter.

F. gravier
   Particule de diamètre compris entre 20 et 2 mm.

D. Kies (m)
   Teilchen zwischen 20 und 2 mm Durchmesser.

Esp. grava
   Partículas entre 20 y 2 mm de diámetro.

P. cascalho
   Partículas de diametro compreendido entre 20 e 2 mm.

I. ghiaia (f)
   Frammenti (di roccia) di diametro compreso tra mm 2
   e mm 20.

Nl. grint
   Deeltjes tussen 20 en 2 mm in doorsnede.

S. grus
   Partiklar mellan 20 och 2 mm i diameter.

Eng.   <u>sand</u>
        Particles of diameter 2-0.02 mm (U.K.).
        Particles of diameter 2-0.05 mm (U.S.).

F.   <u>sable</u>
        Particules de 0,02 à 2 mm de diamètre.

D.   <u>Sand</u> (m)
        Teilchen zwischen 2 und 0,02 mm (Grobsand + Feinsand).

Esp.   <u>arena</u>
        Fracción de la base sólida del suelo constituida por
        partículas cuyo diámetro varía entre 2 y 0,02 mm.

P.   <u>areia</u>
        Partículas terrosas de diâmetro compreendido entre 2
        e 0,02 mm.

I.   <u>sabbia</u>
        Particelle con diametro compreso tra mm 2 e mm 0,02.

Nl.   <u>zand</u>
        Deeltjes met een diameter tussen 2 en 0,016 mm.

S.   <u>sand</u>
        Partiklar mellan 2-0,2 mm i diameter.
       <u>mellansand</u>
        Partiklar mellan 0,6-0,2 mm i diameter.

29

B4

Eng.   <u>coarse sand</u>
        Particles of diameter between 2 and 0.2 mm.

F.   <u>sable grossier</u>
        Particules d'un diamètre compris entre 2 et 0,2 mm.

D.   <u>Grobsand</u> (m)
        Teilchen von einem Durchmesser zwischen 2 und 0,2 mm.

Esp.   <u>arena gruesa</u>
        Partículas entre 2 y 0,2 mm de diámetro.

P.   <u>areia grossa</u>
        Partículas terrosas cujo diâmetro está compreendido entre 2 e 0,2 mm.

I.   <u>sabbia</u> (f) <u>grossa</u>
        Particelle di diametro compreso tra mm 2 e 0,2.

Nl.   <u>grof zand</u>
        Deeltjes met een doorsnede tussen 2 en 0,2 mm.

S.   <u>grovsand</u>
        Partiklar mellan 0,6-2 mm.

Eng. fine sand
        Particles of diameter between 0.2 and 0.02 mm.

F. sable fin
        Particules de diamètre compris entre 0,2 et 0,02 mm.

D. Feinsand (m)
        Teilchen mit einem Durchmesser zwischen 0,2 und 0,02 mm.

Esp. arena fina
        Partículas de diámetro entre 0,2 y 0,02 mm.

P. areia fina
        Partículas de diâmetro compreendido entre 0,2 e 0,02 mm.

I. sabbia (f) fina
        Particelle di diametro compreso tra mm 0,2 e 0,02.

Nl. fijnzand
        Deeltjes met een diameter tussen 0,2 en 0,016 mm.

S. mo
        Partiklar mellan 0,2-0,02 mm.
   grovmo
        Partiklar mellan 0,06-0,2 mm.

B6

Eng. <u>fine earth</u>
Soil passing through 2 mm sieve without grinding
primary particles.

F. <u>terre fine</u>
Terre passant au tamis de 2 mm.

D. <u>Feinerde</u>
Boden, der durch das 2 mm Sieb geht.

Esp. <u>suelo fino</u>
Suelo que pasa por el tamiz de 1 mm ó 2 mm.

P. <u>terra fina</u>
Solo que passa através do crivo de 2 mm.

I. <u>terra</u> (f) <u>fina</u>
Terreno che nella vagliatura passa attraverso maglie
mm 2.

Nl. <u>gezeefde grond</u>
Grond, die in luchtdroge toestand door een 2 mm zeef
is gegaan.

S. <u>finjord</u>
Jord som passerar sikt med 2 mm maskvidd.

Eng. <u>loam</u>
Soil having clay and coarser particles in proportions which usually form a permeable, friable mixture (U.K.). Soil material containing 7-27% clay, 28-50% silt, and less than 52% sand (U.S.).

F. <u>limon</u>
Sol à dominance d'éléments fins, généralement friables.

D. <u>Lehm</u> (m)
Mischung aus Ton, Schluff und Sand in definiertem Verhältnis.

Esp. <u>suelo franco</u>
Suelo que tiene arcilla y partículas gruesas en proporciones tales de formar una mezcla permeable y friable.

P. <u>terra franca</u>
Solo contendo argila e partículas grosseiras em proporções que formam uma mistura permeável e friável.

I. <u>terreno</u> (m) <u>di medio impasto</u> (m)
Terreno che contiene materiali argillosi e particelle più grossolane in proporzioni tali da formare un miscuglio permeabile e friabile.

Nl. <u>zavel</u>
Een Holocene, mariene grond met een kleigehalte tussen ca 7,5% en 25%.
<u>leem</u>
Een Pleistocene of oudere afzetting met wisselend kleigehalte, dat tenminste 10% bedraagt.

S. <u>lättlera</u>
Mineraljord, som innehåller 15-25 viktsprocent ler.
<u>mellanlera</u>
Mineraljord, som innehåller 25-40 viktsprocent ler.

Eng. <u>silt</u>
        Particles of diameter 0.02-0.002 mm (U.K.).
        Particles of diameter 0.05-0.002 mm (U.S.).

F.   <u>limon</u>
        Particule d'un diamètre compris entre 0,02 à 0,002 mm.

D.   <u>Schluff</u> (m)
        Teilchen mit einem mittleren Durchmesser von 0,02-0,002
        mm.

Esp. <u>limo</u>
        Partículas con diám. .ro medio de 0,02 a 0,002 mm.

P.   <u>limo</u>
        Partículas com um diâmetro médio entre 0,02 e 0,002 mm.

I.   <u>limo</u> (m) <u>fine</u>
    <u>fango</u> (m) <u>grosso</u>
        Particelle con un diametro medio compreso tra mm 0,02
        e 0,002.

Nl. <u>stof, sloef, silt</u>
        Deeltjes met een diameter van 0,02 tot 0,002 mm.
    <u>slib</u>
        Deeltjes met een diameter van 0,016 tot 0,002 mm.

S.   <u>mjäla</u>
        Partiklar mellan 0,02-0,002 mm i diameter.
    <u>grovmjäla</u>
        Partiklar mellan 0,02-0,006 mm i diameter.
    <u>finmjäla</u>
        Partiklar mellan 0,06-0,002 mm i diameter.

Eng. silt and clay
  Particles smaller than 0.02 mm that do not settle out
  of water and can be separated by decantation.

F. argile et limon
  Particules au-dessous de 0,02 mm.

D. abschlämmbare Bestandteile (f)
  Durch Schlämmen abtrennbare Bodenteilchen mit einem
  Durchmesser unter 0,02 mm.

Esp. limo y arcilla
  Partículas de diametro inferior a 0,02 mm, que no se
  asientan fuera del agua, y que pueden separarse por
  decantación.

P. limo e argila
  Partículas de diâmetro inferior a 0,02 mm.

I. limo (m) e argilla (f)
  Particelle più piccole di 0,02 mm.

Nl. afslibbare bestanddelen
  Deeltjes kleiner dan 0,016 mm, die in water niet bezin-
  ken en door overgieten kunnen worden afgezonderd.

S. uppslammningsbar fraktion
  Partiklar med diameter mindre än 0,01 mm, frånskilda
  med Kopeckys metod.

Eng. <u>clay</u>
        Particles of diameter less than 0.002 mm.

F. <u>argile</u>
        Particules de diamètre inférieur à 0,002 mm.

D. <u>Ton</u> (m)
        Teilchen mit einem Durchmesser von weniger als
        0,002 mm.

Esp. <u>arcilla</u>
        Partículas de diámetro menor de 0,002 mm.

P. <u>argila</u>
        Partículas de diâmetro inferior a 0,002 mm.

I. <u>argilla</u>
        Particelle del diametro minore di mm 0,002.

Nl. <u>lutum</u>
        Deeltjes met een diameter kleiner dan 0,002 mm.

S. <u>ler</u>
        Partiklar med partikeldiameter $< 0,002$ mm.

Eng. <u>clay fraction</u>
      Clay distinguished from coarser soil particles.

F. <u>fraction argileuse</u>
      Fraction du sol ayant les dimensions de l'argile.

D. <u>Tonfraktion</u> (f)
      Ton im Unterschied zu gröberen Bodenteilchen.

Esp. <u>fracción arcilla</u>
      Arcilla cuando se considera separada de las otras
      partículas del suelo.

P. <u>fracção argilosa</u>
      A argila separada das outras partículas do solo.

I. <u>frazione</u> (f) <u>argillosa</u>
      L'argilla distinta dalle altre particelle del terreno.

Nl. <u>kleifractie</u>
      Het geheel aan deeltjes met een diameter kleiner dan
      0,016 mm ter onderscheiding van het geheel aan zand-,
      resp. aan humusdeeltjes.

S. <u>lerfraktion</u>
      Leret till skillnad från andra jordpartiklar.

Eng. <u>clay colloid</u>
  Clay particles of diameter less than 0.001 mm.

F. ------------

D. <u>Kolloidton</u> (m)
  Teilchen mit einem Durchmesser von weniger als
  0,0002 mm.

Esp. <u>arcilla coloidal</u>
  Partículas de diámetro menor de 0,001 mm.

P. <u>argila coloidal</u>
  Partículas terrosas com dimensões coloidais.

I. <u>argilla</u> (f) <u>colloidale</u>
  Particelle di diametro inferiore a mm 0,001.

Nl. <u>klei colloïd</u>
  Klei-deeltjes met een diameter kleiner dan 0,001 mm.

S. <u>lerkolloid</u>
  Partikel med diameter $< 0,002$ mm.

Eng.   mechanical analysis
>   Particle-size analysis — the determination of fractions
>   by weight or mass, based on the separation of primary
>   soil particles into groups according to "effective" dia-
>   meters.

F.   analyse mécanique
>   Séparation des particules en groupes suivant leur dia-
>   mètre.

D.   mechanische Analyse (f)
>   Ermittlung der Teilchengrösse durch Bestimmung des
>   Äquivalent-Durchmessers mittels Sieb- und Schlämm-
>   Analyse.

Esp.   análisis mecánico
>   Separación de partículas segun su tamaño.

P.   analise mecanica
>   Separação das partículas em classes segundo o tamanho.

I.   analisi meccanica (f)
>   Separazione delle particelle in gruppi distinti per
>   dimensioni.

Nl.   slibanalyse
>   Bepaling der granulaire samenstelling.

S.   mekanisk analys
>   Bestämning av partikelstorleksfördelningen i en jord.

B14

Eng. sedimentation analysis
    Separation of particles depending on rate of settling
    in a fluid.

F. analyse par sédimentation
    Séparation des particules suivant leur vitesse de
    chute dans l' eau.

D. Schlämmanalyse (f)
    Auf der verschiedenen Absetzgeschwindigkeit im Wasser
    beruhende Trennung von Teilchen.

Esp. análisis por sedimentación
    Separación de partículas según la velocidad de deposi-
    ción en el agua.

P. analise de sedimentação
    Separação de partículas segundo a velocidade de sedi-
    mentação.

I. analisi (f) granulometrica per decantazione (f) o levigazione
    Separazione delle particelle a seconda del loro grado di
    sedimentazione nell'acqua.

Nl. sedimentatie analyse
    Scheiding van deeltjes met gebruikmaking van de
    bezinkingssnelheid in water.

S. sedimentationsanalys
    Bestämning av partikelstorleksfördelningen i en jord
    med tillhjälp av partiklarnas fallhastighet i vatten.

40

Eng.   summation curve
A curve plotted with the percentage by weight of particles larger (or smaller) than a given diameter against
diameter.

F.   courbe de sommation
Courbe établie en portant en abscisses les diamètres
des particules constituant le sol, et en ordonnés le
pourcentage de particules dont les dimensions sont
inférieures (ou supérieures) à ces diamètres.

D.   Summenlinie (f)
Methode, die Korngrössenverteilung eines Bodens oder
Sediments graphisch darzustellen.

Esp.   curva aditiva
Expresión gráfica de la composición mecánica.

P.   curva somatória
Método gráfico de expressar a composição mecanica do
solo.

I.   curva (f) granulometrica
Una curva con la percentuale in peso delle particelle
di ogni diametro.

Nl.   sommatiecurve
Manier van voorstellen van de granulaire samenstelling.

S.   summationskurva
En kurva som åskådliggör jordens mekaniska sammansätt-
ning.

B16

Eng.   degree of dispersion
   Extent to which aggregates are broken down to primary
   particles by a given treatment.

F.   degré de dispersion
   Proportion d'agrégats se dislocant en particules
   élémentaires par agitation dans l'eau.

D.   Dispersionsgrad (m)
   Zerteilungsgrad bis zu dem Aggregate dur:h eine
   gegebene Behandlung auseinander brechen.

Esp.   grado de dispersión
   Límite hasta el cual se desmenuzan los agregados por
   agitación con agua.

P.   grau de dispersão
   O grau de separação das partículas dos agregados pro-
   vocada pela agitação com água.

I.   grado (m) di dispersione (f)
   Dimensioni sino alle quali gli aggregati vengono sud-
   divisi per mezzo di agitazione in acqua.

Nl.   dispersiteitsgraad
   Mate waarin aggregaten worden afgebroken door schudden
   met water.

S.   dispersionsgrad
   Den grad till vilken en substans är finfördelad.

Eng.   structure
             Arrangement of soil particles into aggregates.

F.   structure
             Disposition des particules de sol les unes par
             rapport aux autres.

D.   Struktur (f)
        Gefüge (n)
             Die Anordnung von Bodenteilchen im Raum.

Esp.   estructura
             Disposición de las partículas del suelo en agre-
             gados de formas y tamaños característicos.

P.   estrutura
             Aglomeração das partículas do solo em agregados
             de forma e tamanho característicos.

I.   struttura (f)
             Disposizione delle particelle del terreno in
             aggregati di forme e dimensioni caratteristiche.

Nl.   structuur
             Ruimtelijke rangschikking van de gronddeeltjes.

S.   struktur
             Jordpartiklarnas anordning i aggregat av karak-
             teristisk storlek och form.

Eng.   structure index
> Measure obtained by sedimentation with and without pre-
> liminary dispersion (U.K.).
> A soil property which is measurable and may be evaluated
> on a numerical scale and is related to soil structure
> (e.g., aggregation, bulk density, moisture retention,
> penetrometer force) (U.S.).

F.   coefficient de stabilité de la structure
> Comparaison de deux portions granulométriques de même
> dimension obtenues à partir d'un sol avec ou sans dis-
> persion.

D.   Strukturfaktor (m)
> Vermittelst Sedimentation mit und ohne vorherige Disper-
> gierung erhaltener Wert.

Esp.   índice de estructura
> Medida obtenida por sedimentación con y sin dispersión.

P.   coeficiente de estrutura
> Medida obtida por sedimentação com e sem dispersão pre-
> liminar.

I.   coefficiente (m) di struttura (f)
> Misura ottenuta col metodo della sedimentazione con o
> senza una preliminare dispersione.

Nl.   structuurindex
> Maatstaf voor het optreden en voor de verdeling der
> afmetingen van tamelijk bestendige aggregaten, bepaald
> door bezinking zonder en met voorafgaande dispersie.

S.   strukturindex
> Mått som erhålles vid sedimentation med och utan före-
> gående dispergering.

Eng. <u>aggregate</u>
Compound particle of soil.

F. <u>agrégat</u>
Agglomérat de sol dont les conditions de formation
ou de stabilité sont définies.

D. <u>Aggregat</u> (n)
Zusammengesetztes Bodenteilchen.

Esp. <u>agregado</u>
Partícula compuesta del suelo.

P. <u>agregado</u>
Partícula composta do solo.

I. <u>aggregato</u> (m)
Particella complessa del terreno.

Nl. <u>aggregaat</u>
Samengesteld gronddeeltje.

S. <u>aggregat</u>
Består av sammanfogade jordpartiklar.

B20

Eng.   <u>degree of aggregation</u>
      Measure of the proportion in which aggregates are
      present.

F.   <u>coefficient d'agrégation</u>
      Mesure de la proportion d'agrégats.

D.   <u>"Aggregationsgrad"</u> (m)
      Anteil der verschiedenen Aggregatgrössen an der
      Gesamtbodenmasse.

Esp.   <u>grado de agregación</u>
      Medida de la proporción de los agregados presentes.

P.   <u>grau de agregação</u>
      Medida da proporção de agregados.

I.   <u>grado di aggregazione</u>
      Misurazione della quantità di aggregati presenti.

Nl.   <u>mate van aggregatie</u>
      Maat voor de omvang, waarin aggregaten aanwezig zijn.

S.   <u>aggregationsgrad</u>
      Mått på förekomsten av aggregat.

Eng. crumb
> Rounded porous aggregate up to 10 mm in diameter.

F. agglomérat
> Assemblage de particules élémentaires du sol.

D. Krümel (m,n)
> Poröses Aggregat bis zu 10 mm Durchmesser.

Esp. agregado migajoso
> Un agregado poroso y redondeado cuyo diámetro es
> inferior a 10 mm.

P. grumo
> Agregado poroso firme e arredondado de diâmetro
> até 10 mm.

I. glomerulo (m)
> Un aggregato rotondeggiante poroso con diametro
> fino a 10 mm.

Nl. kruimel
> Tamelijk los en poreus aggregaat van afgeronde
> vorm, doorgaans kleiner dan 10 mm.

S. klump
> Ett rundat (poröst) aggregat upp till 10 mm i
> diameter.

Eng. crumb structure
        Consisting of small, soft, porous aggregates of
        irregular shape.

F.   structure grumeleuse
        Constitué de petits agglomérats séparés et poreux,
        de forme régulière plutôt arrondie.

D.   Krümelstruktur (f)
        Überwiegendes Vorhandensein von porösen Aggregaten in
        Krümelgrösse.

Esp. estructura migajosa (grumosa)
        Consistente en agregados pequeños, suaves y porosos de
        forma irregular.

P.   estrutura grumosa
        Estrutura em grumos (agregados porosos, arredondados
        de diâmetro até 10 mm).

I.   struttura (f) glomerulare (lacunare)
        Che consiste di aggregati piccoli, soffici, porosi, di
        forme irregolari.

Nl.   kruimelstructuur
        Structuur, hoofdzakelijk opgebouwd uit kruimels.

S.   kornstruktur
        Struktur uppbyggd av små porösa aggregat som kunna ha
        oregelbunden form.

Eng. <u>granule</u>
Friable rounded aggregate of irregular shape up to
10 mm in diameter.

F. <u>granule</u>
Agglomérat arrondi.(En français pas de spécification
de dimension.)

D. <u>Krümel</u> (m,n)
Poröses Aggregat bis zu 10 mm Durchmesser.

Esp. <u>gránulo</u>
Un agregado redondeado bastante firme de hasta 10 mm
de diámetro.

P. <u>grânulo</u>
Um agregado arredondado e firme de diâmetro menor do
que 10 mm.

I. <u>granulo</u> (m)
Un aggregato rotondeggiante assai saldo di dimensioni
fino a mm 10 di diametro.

Nl. <u>korrel</u>
Een afgerond, behoorlijk hard aggregaat met een diameter tot 10 mm

S. <u>gryn</u>
<u>korn</u>
Ett rundat relativt fast aggregat upp till 10 mm i
diameter.

49

Eng.   granular structure
        Consisting of friable rounded aggregates of irregular
        shape, and of aggregates compounded of smaller aggre-
        gates.

F.   structure granuleuse
        Constitué par de petits agglomérats arrondis.

D.   Krümelstruktur (f)
        Überwiegendes Vorhandensein von porösen Aggregaten in
        Krümelgrösse.

Esp.   estructura granular
        Que consiste ie agregados pequeños, estables y redon-
        deados.

P.   estrutura granulosa
        Constituido por agregados angulosos ou arredondados,
        pequenos e firmes.

I.   struttura (f) granulare
        Che consiste di aggregati piccoli, stabili, arroton-
        dati.

Nl.   hagelstructuur
        Bestaande uit kleine, stevige, afgeronde aggregaten.

S.   grynstruktur
        Består av små fasta, rundade aggregat.

Eng. <u>clod</u>
　　　Lump of soil material.

F. <u>motte</u>
　　　Bloc cohérent du sol.

D. <u>Scholle</u> (f)
　　　Harter, schwerer Klumpen.

Esp. <u>terrón</u>
　　　Un agregado informe, pesado y compacto.

P. <u>torrão</u>
　　　Um agregado pesado e duro.

I. <u>zolla</u> (f)
　　　Un ammasso informe e compatto di terra.

Nl. <u>kluit</u>
　　　Stevig en dicht aggregaat, doorgaans met
　　　scherpe hoeken.

S. <u>jordkoka</u>
　　　Mer eller mindre hård, oregelbundet formad
　　　lösbruten del av marken.

B26

Eng. <u>ultimate particle</u>
   The single particle or organic micelle after complete
   dispersion of aggregates.

F. <u>particule élémentaire</u>
   Particule simple après dispersion complète des agrégats.

D. <u>Primärteilchen</u> (n)
   Das Einzelteilchen nach vollkommener Auseinandertrennung
   der Aggregate.

Esp. <u>partícula elemental</u>
   La partícula individual después de la completa dispersión de los agregados.

P. <u>partícula elementar</u>
   Partícula simples resultante da completa dispersão dos
   agregados.

I. <u>particella</u> (f) <u>elementare</u>
   La particella individuale dopo la completa dispersione
   degli aggregati.

Nl. <u>elementair deeltje</u>
   Het afzonderlijke deeltje na volledige dispersie van de
   aggregaten.

S. <u>primärpartikel</u>
   Enkla partiklar (som erhålles efter fullständig dispersion av aggregat).

Eng. <u>single-grain structure</u>
Physical state of soil in which there is no aggregation
of the separate particles.

F. <u>structure monogranulaire</u>
Assemblage terreux, sans agglomération des particules en
agrégats.

D. <u>Einzelkornstruktur</u> (f)
Lagerung der Einzelteilchen ohne Bildung von Einzel-
aggregaten.

Esp. <u>estructura de grano simple</u>
Estado físico de un suelo en el cual las partículas
existen independientemente unas de otras.

P. <u>estrutura amorfa</u>
<u>estrutura em grãos isolados</u>
<u>sem estrutura</u>
Estado físico do solo em que não há qualquer agregação
das partículas primárias.

I. <u>struttura</u> (f) <u>a granuli isolati</u>
Stato fisico del terreno in cui non c'è aggregazione
delle singole particelle.

Nl. <u>éénkorrelige structuur</u>
Natuurkundige toestand van de grond waarin de deeltjes
afzonderlijk, zonder samenkittingen, liggen.

S. <u>enkelkornstruktur</u>
Strukturtyp, utmärkt av att de enskilda partiklarna
icke bilda aggregat, utan äro fria från varandra.

Section C

SOIL WATER

EAU DU SOL

AGUAS FREATICAS

Eng. <u>moisture</u>
Water that can be removed from soil by heating to 105ºC.

F.   <u>humidité</u>
Eau pouvant être éliminée du sol par le chauffage à
105ºC.

D.   <u>(Gesamt)wassergehalt</u> (m)
Wasser, das aus einem Boden durch Erhitzen auf 105ºC
entfernt werden kann.

Esp. <u>humedad</u>
Agua que puede ser removida del suelo calentándolo a
105ºC.

P.   <u>humidade</u>
Agua que pode ser extraída do solo pelo aquecimento a
105ºC.

I.   <u>umidità</u> (f)
Acqua che può essere scacciata dal terreno riscaldando
a 105ºC per 24-36 ore.

Nl.   <u>vocht</u>
Water, dat uit een grond verwijderd kan worden door
verhitting op 105ºC.

S.   <u>fuktighet</u>
Vatten som kan avlägsnas ur jorden genom upphettning
till 105ºC.

C2

Eng. <u>air-dry</u>
Moisture content in equilibrium with surrounding air.

F. <u>séché à l'air</u>
Sol dont la teneur en eau est en équilibre avec l'atmosphère ambiante.

D. <u>lufttrocken</u>
Feuchtigkeitsgehalt im Gleichgewicht mit der umgebenden Luft.

Esp. <u>secado al aire</u>
Que tiene un bajo contenido de humedad después de quedar expuesto al aire.

P. <u>seco ao ar</u>
Que tem, depois de em equilíbrio com o ar, percentagem baixa de humidade.

I. <u>essicato all'aria</u>
Contenuto idrico in equilibrio con l'aria circostante.

Nl. <u>luchtdroog</u>
Vochtigheidstoestand, in evenwicht met die van de omkringende tamelijk droge atmosfeer (meestal binnenshuis bij kamertemperatuur).

S. <u>lufttorr</u>
Fuktighetshalt i material i jämvikt med vanlig luft.

Eng. __maximum water-holding capacity__
    Amount of water retained by a layer of soil in equili-
    brium with a water table at its lower surface (U.K.).
    Average moisture content of a disturbed sample of soil
    1 cm high after equilibration with a water table into
    which it is immersed 1 mm. The soil cup was removed
    and wiped by Hilgard before weighing (U.S.).

F. __capacité maximum de retention en eau__
    Quantité maximum d'eau que retient une couche de sol.

D. __maximale Wasserkapazität (f)__
    Wassermenge, die eine Bodenschicht in Berührung mit
    einer Wasseroberfläche festhalten kann. (Konventionelle
    Methoden.)

Esp. __capacidad máxima de retención de agua__
    Cantidad de agua que puede absorber una delgada capa de
    suelo.

P. __capacidade maxima de retenção de água__
    Quantidade maxima de água que uma camada do solo pode
    absorver.

I. __capacità (f) idrica massima__
  __capacità di saturazione__
    Quantità d'acqua trattenuta da uno strato di terreno in
    equilibrio con la falda freatica alla sua faccia
    inferiore.

Nl. __maximale water capaciteit__
    Vochtgehalte van een dunne laag grond, waarvan de onder-
    kant samenvalt met een (kunstmatige) grondwaterspiegel.

S. __maximal vattenkapacitet__
    Den mängd vatten ett tunt jordlager kan suga upp och
    kvarhålla.

C4

Eng.　**field capacity**
　　　　Water held in a well drained soil after excess has
　　　　drained away and rate of downward movement has
　　　　materially decreased.

F.　　**capacité de rétention au champ**
　　　　Eau retenue par le sol après drainage.

D.　　**Feldkapazität** (f), **(Wasserkapazität)** (f)
　　　　Wassermenge die im natürlichen Bodenverband festgehalten
　　　　werden kann. (Konventionelle Methode.)

Esp.　**capacidad de campo**
　　　　Agua retenida por el suelo después de haber drenado el
　　　　agua gravitante.

P.　　**capacidade de campo**
　　　　A água retida no solo depois de ter sido dranado o
　　　　excesso de água gravitacional e de o movimento des-
　　　　cendente ter decrescido substancialmente.

I.　　**acqua** (f) **d'imbibizione** (f)
　　　　Acqua trattenuta dal terreno dopo che ne e stata
　　　　drenata l'acqua di falda ovvero l'acqua di saturazione.

Nl.　　**water capaciteit**
　　　　Door de grond vastgehouden water nadat het overtollige
　　　　is afgevoerd.

S.　　**fältkapacitet**
　　　　Den största vattenmängd en jord kan hålla sedan fritt
　　　　vatten avrunnit.

Eng. moisture equivalent
Percent moisture retained against centrifugal force
1000 times gravity.

F. humidité équivalente
Pourcentage d'humidité retenue pour une force centri-
fuge égale à 1000 fois la gravité.

D. "Feuchtigkeits-Aequivalent" (n),(minimale Wasserkapazität)(f)
Prozent Feuchtigkeit, die gegen eine Zentrifugalkraft,
die 1000 mal grösser als die Schwerkraft ist, zurückgehalten wird.

Esp. equivalente de humedad
Por ciento de humedad retenido por un suelo sometido
a una fuerza centrífuga de 1000 veces la gravedad.

P. equivalent de humidade
Percentagem de humidade retida depois de sujeitar o
solo a uma força centrifuga 1000 vezes maior que a
da gravidade.

I. equivalente (m) d'umidità (f)
Percentuale di umidità trattenuta dal terreno sotto-
posto a centrifugazione tale da sviluppare una forza
(accelerazione) 1000 volte maggiore quella della gravità.

Nl. vochtequivalent
Het percentage vocht, dat wordt vastgehouden bij een
centrifugale kracht van 1000 maal de zwaartekracht.

S. fuktighetsekvivalent
Fuktighet som kvarhålles med en kraft minst 1000 ggr
starkare än tyngdkraften.

C6

Eng. <u>hygroscopic coefficient</u>
        Amount of moisture held by soil after exposure to high
        humidity for 24 hours at 25°C.

F. <u>coefficient d'hygroscopicité</u>
        Quantité de vapeur d'eau absorbée par le sol dans des
        conditions définies.

D. <u>Hygroskopizitätszahl</u> (f)
        Die Menge an Wasserdampf die unter bestimmten Bedin-
        gungen vom trockenen Boden absorbiert wird. (Konven-
        tionelle Methoden.)

Esp. <u>coeficiente higroscópico</u>
        Cantidad de vapor de agua absorbido por el suelo bajo
        condiciones especificas.

P. <u>coeficiente higroscópico</u>
        Quantidade de água absorvida pelo solo em determinadas
        condições.

I. <u>coefficiente</u> (m) <u>di igroscopicità</u>
        Quantità di umidità assorbita dal terreno dopo esser
        stato esposto in ambiente ad alta umidità per 24 ore
        a 25°C.

Nl. <u>hygroscopiciteit</u>
        Vochtgehalte, waarbij een grondmonster in evenwicht is
        met een bepaalde (conventionele) waterdampspanning.

S. <u>hygroskopicitet,(hygroskopicitetskoeff.)</u>
        Den mängd vatten, som jorden binder under vissa bestämda
        förhållanden.

Eng. fifteen-atmosphere percentage
Percentage of water retained by a wetted soil sample
after attainment of hydraulic equilibrium at a water
tension of 15 atmospheres.

F. --------------------------------
Humidité d'un sol en équilibre avec une force de
15 atmosphères.

D. fünfzehn-Atmosphären-Gehalt (m)
Feuchtigkeit, die von einem zuvor wassergesättigten
Boden im Gleichgewicht mit einer Druckmembran bei
15 Atmosphären Druck zurückgehalten wird.

Esp. porcentaje de 15 atmósferas
La humedad retenida por un suelo cuando está en equilibrio con una membrana sometida a una presión de 15
atmósferas.

P. percentagem a 15 atmosferas
Humidade retida pelo solo em equilíbrio com uma membrana sujeita à pressão de 15 atmosferas.

I. percentuale (f) di 15 atmosfere (f p)
Umidità trattenuta dal terreno umido quando sia in
equilibrio con una membrana a pressione, alla pressione di 15 atmosfere.

Nl. vochtgehalte bij 15 at.
Vochtgehalte van een oorspronkelijke vochtige grond,
nadat er op een membraan door een overdruk van 15 at.
zoveel mogelijk water aan is onttrokken.

S. fuktighet vid 15 atm. tryck
femton-atmosfärsgränsen
Den fuktighet som kvarhålles av en våt jord i jämvikt
med en tryckmembran vid 15 atm. tryck.

63

Eng.   <u>sticky point</u>
Maximum moisture content at which kneaded soil ceases
to stick to a knife.

F.   <u>point d'adhésivité</u>
Teneur en eau pour laquelle une terre pétrie cesse
d'adhérer à une lame de couteau.

D.   <u>Klebepunkt</u> (m)
Höchster Feuchtigkeitsgehalt, bei dem gekneteter Boden
gerade noch an einem Messer festklebt.

Esp.   <u>punto de adherencia</u>
Contenido de humedad con el cual un suelo amasado cesa
de pegarse a un cuchillo.

P.   <u>ponto de aderência</u>
Teor em humidade a que o solo amassado deixa de aderir
à espátula.

I.   <u>limite</u> (m) <u>di adesione</u> (f)
Contenuto idrico al quale il terreno impastato cessa di
rimanere attaccato al coltello.

Nl.   <u>kleefgrens</u>
Vochtgehalte waarbij een geknede grond ophoudt aan een
mes te kleven.

S.   <u>vidhäftningspunkt</u>
Fuktighetshalt vid vilken en knådad jord upphör att
häfta vid en kniv.

Eng.   upper plastic limit
           Minimum moisture content at which soil will barely flow
           under a standard stress.

F.   limite supérieure de plasticité
           Teneur en eau à partir de laquelle le sol devient fluide.

D.   obere Plastizitätsgrenze (f)
      Zerfliessgrenze (f)
           Feuchtigkeitsgehalt, bei dem eine steife Paste — unter
           genormtem Druck — sich gerade eben verflüssigt.

Esp.   límite superior de plasticidad
           Contenido de humedad al cual una pasta firme se trans-
           forma en un barro fluido.

P.   limite superior de plasticidade
           Quantidade de humidade a que uma pasta pegajosa se torna
           fluida.

I.   limite (m) superiore di plasticità (f)
           Contenuto in acqua per cui una pasta perde la consis-
           tenza solida e assume quella di un fluido molto viscoso
           (come mota) e si moverà solamente sotto una forza.

Nl.   vloeigrens
           Vochtgehalte waarbij een stijve pasta door kloppen
           begint te vervloeien.

S.   övre plastisk gräns
           Fuktighetsinnehåll vid vilket en lerjord övergår från
           plastisk till halvflytande konsistens.

Eng.   <u>lower plastic limit</u>
Minimum moisture content permitting deformation of a
small soil sample without rupture (Atterberg).

F.   <u>limite inférieure de plasticité</u>
Limite inférieure de l'humidité à partir de laquelle
se produit une déformation sans rupture, cette valeur
doit être précisée par un test conventionnel (Atterberg).

D.   <u>untere Plastizitätsgrenze</u> (f)
Minimaler Feuchtigkeitsgehalt, der Formveränderungen
ohne Bruch gerade noch erlaubt. (Konventionelle Probe
nach Atterberg.)

Esp.   <u>límite inferior de plasticidad</u>
Contenido de humedad que permite la deformación sin
ruptura (Atterberg).

F.   <u>limite mínimo de plasticidade</u>
A mínima quantidade de humidade que permite deformação
do solo sem rutura (Atterberg).

I.   <u>limite</u> (m) <u>inferiore di plasticità</u> (f)
<u>limite</u> (m) <u>plastico inferiore</u>
Contenuto idrico che consente la deformazione senza
rottura (Atterberg).

Nl.   <u>uitrolgrens</u>
Vochtgehalte waarbij bij herhaald uitrollen van de vochtige grond tot een dunne staaf deze begint te brokkelen.

S.   <u>nedre plastisk gräns</u>
Lägsta vattenhalt tillåtande omformning utan bristning
(Atterberg).

Eng.   wilting point (U.K.)
wilting percentage (U.S.)
The maximum moisture percentage of soil that will induce
permanent wilting of plants.

F.   pointe de flétrissement
Taux d'humidité pour lequel les feuilles se fanent sans
pouvoir reprendre leur turgescence dans une atmosphère
saturée.

D.   permanenter Welkepunkt (m)
Wassergehalt des Bodens, bei dem die Blätter einer Test-
pflanze erschlaffen und sich nicht wieder erholen, wenn
sie 24 Stunden lang einer wasserdampfgesättigten Atmos-
phäre ausgesetzt werden.

Esp.   índice de marchitez
coeficiente de marchitamiento
Mínimo contenido de humedad del suelo, aprovechable por
las plantas.

P.   coeficiente de emurchecimento
Teor de humidade do solo quando as folhas murcham
irreversívelmente.

I.   punto (m) di avvizzimento (m) (appassimento) (m) permanente
Contenuto di umidità del terreno al quale le foglie si
ripiegano senza poter più riacquistare il turgore dopo
esser state esposte per 24 ore in un'atmosfera satura
di vapor d'acqua.

Nl.   verwelkingspunt
Vochtgehalte van de grond, waarbij de bladeren van een
erop groeiende proefplant slap gaan hangen, zonder zich
na verblijf van 24 uur in een met waterdamp verzadigde
atmosfeer te herstellen.

S.   vissningspunkt
Det högsta fuktighetsinnehåll i jorden, vid vilket
växterna vissna utan att kunna återställas.

Eng.　lento-capillary point
　　　　　Vague term applied to moisture content at which movement
　　　　　of water through soil becomes slow.　(Obsolete.)

F.　point lento-capillaire
　　　　　Teneur en eau à partir de laquelle le mouvement de l'eau
　　　　　à travers le sol se ralentit.　(Non utilisé en français.)

L　lentokapillarer Punkt
　　　　　Feuchtigkeitsgehalt, bei dem die Bewegung von Wasser in
　　　　　flüssiger Form aufhört.

Esp.　punto lento capilar
　　　　　Contenido de humedad con el cual el movimiento del agua
　　　　　a través del suelo se hace lento.

P.　ponto lento capilar
　　　　　Percentagem de humidade para a qual o movimento da água
　　　　　no solo se torna vagaroso.

I.　punto (m) di capillarità (f) rallentata
　　　　　Grado del contenuto idrico per cui il movimento
　　　　　dell'acqua attraverso il terreno diviene lento.

Nl.　lento capillaire punt
　　　　　Het vochtgehalte, waarbij de beweging van water door de
　　　　　grond langzaam wordt.

S.　lentokapillär punkt
　　　　　Fuktighetsinnehåll vid vilket vattenrörelsen genom
　　　　　jorden blir mycket långsam.

Eng. <u>gravitational water</u>
>   Water that moves in the soil under force of gravity.

F. <u>eau de gravité</u>
>   Eau se déplaçant sous l'action de la pesanteur.

D. <u>Gravitationswasser</u> (n)
>   Wasser, das — nur der Schwerkraft gehorchend — im
>   spannungsfreien Hohlraumvolumen versickert.

Esp. <u>agua gravitante</u>
>   Agua que se mueve hacia abajo dentro de la zona de
>   aireación.

P. <u>água gravitacional</u>
>   Água que não é retida pelo solo, infiltrando-se sob
>   a acção da gravidade.

I. <u>acqua</u> (f) <u>di falda</u> (f)
>   <u>acqua di gravità</u>
>   <u>acqua gravitazionale</u>
>   Acqua che si sposta verso il basso entro la zona
>   aerata.

Nl. <u>gravitatie water</u>
>   Water dat zich in de geaereerde zône naar beneden
>   beweegt.

S. <u>fritt vatten</u>
>   Vatten som rör sig i jorden under inverkan av tyngd-
>   kraften.

Eng. <u>film water</u>
Water retained in layers thicker than one or two mole-
cules on the surface of particles in unsaturated soil.

F. <u>eau pelliculaire</u>
Eau adhérant aux particules du sol.

D. <u>Haftwasser</u> (n)
Wasser, das längere Zeit gegen die Schwerkraft an den
Bodenteilchen haftet.

Esp. <u>peliculas de agua</u>
Agua que se adhiere a las partículas del suelo.

P. <u>película de água</u>
Água aderente às partículas do solo.

I. <u>acqua</u> (f) <u>di adesione</u> (f)
Acqua che adrenisce alle particelle del suolo.

Nl. <u>sorptiewater</u>
Water dat door krachten uitsluitend van de grond-
deeltjes zelf uitgaande aan deze wordt gebonden.

S. <u>adhesionsvatten</u>
Vatten som häftar vid jordpartiklarna.

Eng.

Hydration water of exchangeable ions.

F.

Eau d'hydratation des ions échangeables.

D.   Schwarmwasser (n)
Hydratationswasser der austauschbaren Ionen

Esp.

Agua de hidratación de los iones intercambiables.

P.

Água de hidratação dos iões de troca

I.

Acqua d'idratazione degli ioni scambiabili.

Nl.

Hydradatiewater van de uitwisselbare basen.

S.

Utbytbara joners hydrationsvatten.

Eng. <u>capillary water</u>
        Water retained in pores by surface tension.

F. <u>eau capillaire</u>
        Eau retenue dans les pores.

D. <u>Kapillarwasser</u> (n)
        In den von den Bodenteilchen gebildeten Hohlräumen
        unter dem Einfluss der Oberflächenspannung fest-
        gehaltenes Wasser.

Esp. <u>agua capilar</u>
        Agua retenida en los poros.

P. <u>água capilar</u>
        Água retida nos poros.

I. <u>acqua</u> (f) <u>di capillarità</u> (f)
        Acqua trattenuta dai pori.

Nl. <u>capillair water</u>
        Bodemwater, dat onder invloed van capillaire krachten
        verkeert.

S. <u>kapillärvatten</u>
        Vatten som kvarhålles i porerna, på grund av att
        vätskemenisker utbildas.

Eng. capillary potential
>   A number representing the work of moving a unit mass of
>   water from the soil to an arbitrary reference location
>   and state.

F.   potential capillaire
>   Hauteur en centimètre à laquelle serait élevé 1 gr d'eau
>   par la différence entre l'énergie libre de ce gramme
>   d'eau et l'énergie de cette eau après fixation.

D.   Kapillarpotential (n)
>   Eine Zahl, welche die Anziehungskraft von Boden für
>   Wasser ausdrückt.

Esp. potencial capilar
>   Un número que representa el poder de atracción del suelo
>   por el agua.

P.   potencial capilar
>   Número representativo da força do retenção do solo para
>   a água.

I.   potenziale (m) della capillarità (f)
>   Numero che rappresenta l'attrazione del terreno per
>   l'acqua.

Nl.   waterspanningspotentiaal
>   capillariteitspotentiaal
>   Getal dat een vochtigheidstoestand van de bodem weer-
>   geeft en samenhangt met de kracht, die nodig is om in
>   die toestand water aan de bodem te onttrekken.

S.   kapillär potential
>   Uttryck för den kraft eller det tryck varmed vatten
>   hålles i jorden vid angiven vattenhalt mätt i cm vatten-
>   pelare.

Eng. pF

Common logarithm of the height in centimetres of a
column of water corresponding to the free-energy
difference between free water and that held by soil,
excluding the effect of salts, expressed on a gravitational scale.

F. pF

Logarithme décimal du potentiel capillaire.

D. pF

Der dekadische Logarithmus des Kapillarpotentials.

Esp. pF

Medida de la fuerza necesaria para extraer agua del
suelo.

P. pF

Logaritmo decimal do potencial capilar.

I. pF

Logaritmo dell'altezza in centimetri della colonna
d'acqua corrispondente alla suzione necessaria per
estrarre l'acqua dal terreno.

Nl. pF

Gewone logarithme van de in cm water gemeten druk,
welke aangewend moet worden om water aan de bodem
te onttrekken.

S. pF

Kapillärpotentials logaritm.

Eng. capillary fringe
      Part of the soil immediately above the water table in
      which suction pressure is linearly related to distance
      from water table.

F.   frange capillaire
      Hauteur de sol immédiatement au-dessus de plan d'eau,
      dans laquelle la succion est en relation linéaire avec
      la distance à ce plan d'eau.

D.   "Kapillar-Zone" (f)
      Unmittelbar oberhalb des Grundwasserspiegels liegende
      Bodenschicht, in der sich der Saugdruck linear mit der
      Entfernung vom Grundwasserstand ändert.

Esp. "faja capilar"
      Parte del suelo inmediatamente encima de la capa
      freática en la cual la presión de succión y la distancia
      a dicha capa, guardan una relación lineal.

P.   franja capilar
      Parte do solo imediatamente acima da toalha freática
      em que a sucção está linearmente relacionada com a dis-
      tância àquela toalha.

I.   frangia (f) capillare
      Parte del terreno immediatamente sopra la falda
      freatica in cui la pressione di suzione è interrelata
      linearmente con la distanza dalla falda freatica.

Nl.   capillaire zone
      Laag onmiddellijk boven de grondwaterspiegel, waarin
      water door capillaire krachten van de grondwaterspiegel
      uit kan opstijgen.

S.   kapillärzon
      Den zon i marken omedelbart över grundvattenytan i
      vilken ett linjärt samband råder mellan sugtryck och
      avstånd till grundvattenytan.

Eng. <u>soil-moisture tension</u>
<u>suction</u>
Pressure deficiency of soil water.

F. <u>tension de l'eau</u>
Diminution de l'énergie libre de l'eau par sa liaison
avec le sol.

D. <u>"Bodenwasserspannung"</u> (f)
Saugkraft des Bodens beim jeweiligen Wassergehalt.

Esp. <u>tensión de humedad del suelo</u>
Deficit de tensión de vapor en un suelo no saturado.

P. <u>tensão da humidade do solo</u>
Pressão negativa da água num solo não saturado.

I. <u>tensione</u> (f) <u>del vapore</u> (m) <u>acqueo, del terreno</u> (m)
Deficienza di pressione del vapore acqueo in un terreno
non saturo.

Nl. <u>waterspanning in de bodem</u>
Onder-, resp. overdruk van het water in de bodem.

S. <u>(jordens)sugförmåga</u>
Den kraft varmed en icke vattenmättad jord tager till
sig vatten.

Eng. heat of wetting
        Heat evolved during the adsorption of water by soil
        colloids when a dry soil is wetted.

F. chaleur d'humectation
        Chaleur dégagée par l'humectation d'un sol sec.

D. Benetzungswärme
        Die bei der Befeuchtung des trockenen Bodens auftre-
        tende Wärme infolge Adsorption von Wasser an Boden-
        kolloiden.

Esp. calor de humedecimiento
        Calor desprendido durante la adsorción de agua por los
        coloides del suelo al humedecer un suelo seco.

P. calor de humedecimento
        Calor libertado durante a adsorção de água pelos
        colóides do solo quando se humedece um solo sêco.

I. calore (m) di inumidimento (m)
        Calore svolto durante l'assorbimento di acqua da parte
        dei colloidi del terreno quando un terreno asciutto
        viene inumidito.

Nl. bevochtigingswarmte
        Warmte, vrijkomend bij opname van water door de bodem-
        colloïden.

S. befuktningsvärme
        Värme som frigöres vid vattensorptionen när en torr
        jord fuktas.

Eng.   ground water
          Water that fills all interstices below the water table.

F.   nappe phréatique
          Nappe d'eau remplissant tous les interstices (du sol)
          au-dessous d'une certaine profondeur.

D.   Grundwasser (m)
          Wasser, das von einer gewissen Tiefe ab alle Bodenhohl-
          räume füllt.

Esp.   agua subterránea
          Agua que llena todos los intersticios debajo de cierta
          profundidad.

P.   toalha de água
       toalha freática
       lençol freático
          Água que enche todos os interstícios abaixo de certo
          nível.

I.   acqua (f) freatica
          Acqua che riempie gli interstizi al di sotto di una
          certa profondità.

Nl.   grondwater
          Het water beneden het phreatisch oppervlak, staande
          onder een druk groter dan 1 at.

S.   grundvatten
          Vatten som fyller hålrummen i jorden under en viss
          nivå, grundvattenytan.

Eng. <u>water table</u>
>   The upper free surface of ground water; locus of points
>   in soil water at which the hydraulic pressure equals the
>   atmospheric pressure.

F. <u>plan d'eau</u>
>   Niveau supérieur de la nappe phréatique.

D. <u>Grundwasserspiegel</u> (m)
>   Die Oberfläche des Grundwassers.

Esp. <u>capa freática</u>
>   El nivel superior del agua subterránea.

P. <u>toalha de água</u>
   <u>toalha freática</u>
   <u>lençol freático</u>
   <u>nível freático</u>
>   O limite superior da **região** do solo ou do material sub-
>   jacente completamente saturado pela água.

I. <u>livello</u> (m) <u>della falda</u> (f) <u>freatica</u>
>   La superficie superiore delle acque che impregnano gli
>   strati del sottosuolo; il punto in cui la pressione
>   idraulica eguaglia la pressione atmosferica.

Nl. <u>phreatisch vlak</u>
>   Het bovenste oppervlak van het grondwater, waarin de
>   druk gelijk is aan één atmosfeer.

S. <u>grundvattenyta</u>
>   Grundvattnets fria övre yta.

Eng. <u>waterlogging</u>
State of being saturated with water.

F. <u>saturation du sol par l'eau</u>
Fait qu'un sol possède tous ses espaces lacunaires
remplis d'eau.

D. <u>Vernässung</u> (f)
Zustand der Übersättigung mit Wasser.

Esp. <u>anegamiento</u>
Estado de saturación con agua.

P. <u>saturação com água</u>
<u>encharcamento</u>
Stado de saturação com água.

I. <u>ristagno</u> (m)
<u>impregnazione</u> (f)
Il fatto di essere saturo d'acqua.

Nl. <u>wateroverlast</u>
Staat van verzadiging met water.

S. <u>försumpning</u>
Vattendränkning av jord under längre tid.

Eng.   infiltration
        Downward movement of water into soil.

F.   infiltration
        Pénétration de l'eau dans le sol.

D.   Versickerung (f)
        Das Eindringen des Wassers in den Boden.

Esp.   infiltración
        El movimiento del agua en el suelo.

P.   infiltração
        O movimento descendente da água do solo.

I.   infiltrazione (f)
        Il movimento dell'acqua per cui essa penetra il terreno.

Nl.   infiltratie
        Het brengen van water in de grond.

S.   infiltration
        Vattnets nedträngande i jorden.

Séction D

CHEMISTRY

CHIMIE

QUIMICA

Eng.   loss on ignition
        Loss in weight caused by heating to redness soil pre-
        viously dried at 105°C.

F.   perte au feu
        Perte de poids due au chauffage au rouge d'un sol pré-
        alablement séché à 105°C.

D.   Glühverlust (m)
        Gewichtsverlust dadurch hervorgerufen, dass vorher bei
        105°C getrocknetes Material auf Rotglut erhitzt wird.

Esp.   pérdida por calcinación
        Pérdida de peso provocada por calentamiento al rojo de
        un material previamente desecado a 105°C.

P.   perda por calcinação
        Perda de peso do solo quando aquecido ao rubro referida
        ao peso seco a 105°C.

I.   perdita (f) al fuoco (m)
        Perdita in peso scaldando al rosso del materiale pre-
        cedentemente essiccato a 105°C.

Nl.   gloeiverlies
        Gewichtsverlies veroorzaakt door verhitting tot rode
        gloed van een stof, die eerst bij 105°C is gedroogd.

S.   glödgningsförlust
        Viktsförlust vid glödgning av ett förut vid 105°C torkat
        prov.

D2

Eng. <u>carbon-nitrogen ratio</u>
Weight ratio of organic carbon to total nitrogen.

F. <u>rapport carbone-azote</u>
% C/% N.

D. <u>Kohlenstoff-Stickstoff-Verhältnis</u> (n)
% C/% N.

Esp. <u>relación carbono-nitrógeno</u>
Valor obtenido al dividir el porcentaje de carbono
orgánico entre el porcentaje de nitrógeno existentes
en el suelo.

P. <u>relação carbono azoto</u>
% C/% N.

I. <u>rapporto</u> (m) <u>carbonio</u> (m) <u>azoto</u> (m)
% C/% N.

Nl. <u>koolstof-stikstof verhouding</u>
% C/% N.

S. <u>kol-kväve kvot</u>
% C/% N.

Eng. <u>silica-sesquioxide ratio</u>
  The molecular ratio $SiO_2/(Al_2O_3+Fe_2O_3) = SiO_2/R_2O_3$.

F. <u>rapport silice-sesquioxydes</u>
  $SiO_2/(Al_2O_3+Fe_2O_3) = SiO_2/R_2O_3$ (rapport moléculaire).

D. <u>Kieselsäure-Sesquioxyd-Verhältnis</u> (n)
  Das Molecularverhältnis $SiO_2/(Al_2O_3+Fe_2O_3) = SiO_2/R_2O_3$.

Esp. <u>relación sílice sesquióxidos</u>
  Cociente resultante de dividir un quebrado de quebrado
  cuyos términos se obtienen en la siguiente forma:
  (a) el numerador, dividiendo el porcentaje de SiO_2
  entre su peso molecular; (b) el denominador, sumando
  los cocientes obtenidos al dividir el porcentaje de
  Fe_2O_3 y de Al_2O_3 entre sus respectivos pesos moleculares.

P. <u>relação sílica sesquióxidos</u>
  $SiO_2/(Al_2O_3+Fe_2O_3) = SiO_2/R_2O_3$.

I. <u>rapporto</u> (m) <u>silice sesquiossido</u>
  Il rapporto molecolare $SiO_2/(Al_2O_3+Fe_2O_3) = SiO_2/R_2O_3$.

Nl. <u>kiezelzuur-sesquioxyden verhouding</u>
  $SiO_2/(Al_2O_3+Fe_2O_3) = SiO_2/R_2O_3$.

S. <u>kiselsyra-seskvioxidkvot</u>
  $SiO_2/(Al_2O_3+Fe_2O_3) = SiO_2/R_2O_3$.

Eng. <u>allitic</u>
Describes soils from which silica has been removed and
in the clay fraction of which Al and Fe compounds pre-
dominate.

F. <u>allites</u>
Sols dans lesquels le rapport silice/sesquioxydes est
inférieur à 1.

D. <u>allitisch</u>
Bezeichnung für Böden mit hohem Anteil an freien Sesquioxyden (Al_2O_3 + Fe_2O_3), silikatische Verbindungen treten
zurück (Laterit).

Esp. <u>alítico</u>
Dícese de aquellos suelos en los que ha habido una pérdida de sílice y en cuya fracción arcilla predominan compuestos de aluminio y hierro.

P. <u>alítico</u>
Relativo a solos em que a sílica foi removida e onde
predominam os compostos de ferro e alumínio na fracção
argilosa.

I. <u>allitico</u> (m)
Designazione di terreni dai quali la silice è stata
rimossa e la frazione d'argilla è caratterizzata per
la predominanza di ferro e di alluminio.

Nl. <u>allitisch</u>
Beschrijft gronden waaruit het kiezelzuur is verwijderd
en in welker klei fractie Al en Fe verbindingen domi-
neren,

S. <u>allitisk</u>
Förvittringstyp i tropikerna. Anrikning av seskvioxider
på grund av urlakning av kiselsyra.

Eng. **siallitic**
    Describes soils with siliceous clay minerals.

F. **siallites**
    Désignation des sols dans lesquels le rapport $\frac{SiO_2}{R_2O_3}$ est supérieur à 2.

D. **siallitisch**
    Bezeichnung für Böden mit silikatischen Tonbestand-teilen.

Esp. **sialitico**
    Refiérese a los suelos cuyos minerales de arcilla son de naturaleza sílicea.

P. **sialítico**
    Relativo aos solos com minerais de argila siliciosos.

I. **siallitico** (m)
    Designazione di terreni con minerali d'argille silicee.

Nl. **siallitisch**
    Beschrijft (gronden met) klei mineralen, die silicium en aluminium in ongeveer aequivalente hoeveelheden bevatten.

S. **siallitisk**
    Förvittringstyp i tempererat klimat, under bildning av Si-Al-lermineral.

D6

Eng. <u>lateritic</u>
    Containing much sesquioxide but little combined silica.

F. <u>latéritique</u>
    Contenant beaucoup de sesquioxyde mais peu de silice.

D. <u>lateritisch</u>
    Viel Sesquioxyde aber wenig Kieselsäure enthaltend.

Esp. <u>laterítico</u>
    Que contiene mucho sesquióxido, pero poca sílice.

P. <u>laterítico</u>
    Contendo muitos sesquióxidos e pouca sílica.

I. <u>lateritico</u>
    Che contiene molti sesquiossidi ma poca silice.

Nl. <u>lateritisch</u>
    Veel sesquioxyden en weinig kiezelzuur bevattend.

S. <u>lateritisk</u>
    Innehåller rikligt med seskvioxider men ringa mängd
    kiselsyra.

Eng. <u>clay complex</u>
   Clay distinguished from humus.

F. <u>complexe argileux</u>
   Argile distinguée de l'humus.

D. <u>Tonkomplex</u>
   Ton im Unterschied zum Humus.

Esp. <u>complejo arcilloso</u>
   Arcilla diferenciada del humus.

P. <u>complexo argiloso</u>
   A argila distinta do humus.

I. <u>complesso argilloso</u> (m)
   L'insieme delle particelle argillose
   distinto dall'umus.

Nl. <u>kleicomplex</u>
   Klei, onderscheiden van humus.

S. <u>lerkomplex</u>
   Leret till skillnad från humusen.

D8

Eng. **acidoid**
Colloid displaying acidic properties.

F. **acidoïde**
Constituant du sol susceptible de se comporter comme un acide.

D. **Azidoid** (n)
Bodenkolloid mit sauren Eigenschaften.

Esp. **"acidoide"**
Dícese de los coloides del suelo que exhiben propiedades ácidas.

P. **acidoide**
Coloide do solo que apresenta propriedades dos ácidos.

I. **acidoide** (m)
Colloide del suolo che dimostra proprietà acide.

Nl. **acidoid**
Kolloid (in de grond) met zuurachtige (basen-bindende) eigenschappen.

S. **acidoid**
Kolloidal substans som uppvisar sura egenskaper.

Eng. <u>basoid</u>
          Colloid displaying basic properties.

F.   <u>basoïde</u>
          Constituant du sol susceptible de se comporter
          comme une base.

D.   <u>Basoid</u> (n)
          Bodenkolloid mit basischen Eigenschaften.

Esp. <u>basoide</u>
          Dícese de los coloides del suelo que exhiben
          propiedades básicas.

P.   <u>basoide</u>
          Coloide do solo que apresenta propriedades
          das bases.

I.   <u>basoide</u> (m)
          Colloide del terreno che dimostra proprietà
          basiche.

Nl.   <u>basoid</u>
          Kolloid (in de grond) met basische (zuur-
          bindende) eigenschappen.

S.   <u>basoid</u>
          Kolloidal substans som uppvisar basiska
          egenskaper.

Eng.　<u>ampholytoid</u>
　　　　Colloid having both acidic and basic properties.

F.　　<u>ampholytoïde</u>
　　　　Colloïde qui peut avoir une charge prédominante
　　　　+ ou - .

D.　　<u>Ampholytoid</u> (n)
　　　　Kolloid, das sowohl als Säure wie als Base reagieren
　　　　kann.

Esp.　<u>anfotérico</u>
　　　　Dícese de los coloides que tienen propiedades tanto
　　　　de ácido como de base.

P.　　<u>anfotérico</u>
　　　　Coloide possuindo propriedades ácidas e básicas.

I.　　<u>anfolitoide</u> (m)
　　　　<u>anfoteroide</u> (m)
　　　　Colloide che può avere predominante una carica + o - .

Nl.　　<u>ampholytoid</u>
　　　　Kolloid (in de grond) met zowel zuurachtige als
　　　　basische eigenschappen.

S.　　<u>amfolytoid</u>
　　　　Kolloidal substans som äger både bas- och syraegen-
　　　　skaper.

Eng.　<u>double layer</u>
　　　　Arrangement of ions in two oppositely charged layers
　　　　near the surface of a clay particle.

F.　　<u>couche double</u>
　　　　Groupement des ions en deux couches de charges opposées
　　　　au voisinage d'une interface solide-liquide.

D.　　<u>Doppelschicht</u> (f)
　　　　Anordnung von Ionen in entgegengesetzt geladenen zwei
　　　　Schichten nahe der Oberfläche eines Tonteilchens.

Esp.　<u>doble capa</u>
　　　　Distribución de los iones en dos capas de cargas opues-
　　　　tas cerca de la superficie de una partícula de arcilla.

P.　　<u>camada dupla</u>
　　　　Arranjo dos iões em duas camadas junto da superfície da
　　　　partícula de argila.

I.　　<u>doppio strato</u> (m)
　　　　Disposizione degli ioni in due strati vicino alla super-
　　　　ficie della particella o granulo d'argilla, o micella.

Nl.　<u>dubbellaag</u>
　　　　..gschikking van ionen in twee tegengesteld geladen
　　　　lagen aan het oppervlak van een kolloid (in de grond).

S.　　<u>dubbelskikt</u>
　　　　Den teoretiska anordning av joner i och vid en fasgräns.

D12

Eng.   **exchange acidity**
   Acidity produced by treating soil with a solution of a
   neutral salt.

F.   **acidité d'échange**
   Acidité produite en traitant le sol avec une solution
   d'un sel neutre d'acide forte et de base forte, et
   résultant de l'échange entre le cation métallique du
   sel et les cations Hydrogène fixés par le complexe
   absorbant du sol.

D.   **Austauschacidität**
   Fähigkeit saurer Böden, aus Neutralsalzen die Säure in
   Freiheit zu setzen.

Esp.   **acidez de cambio**
   Acidez obtenida al tratar un suelo con una solución
   de sal neutra.

P.   **acidez de troca**
   Acidez produzida pelo tratamento do solo com uma solu-
   ção de um sal neutro.

I.   **acidità (f) di scambio (m)**
   Acidità prodotta trattando un terreno con una soluzione
   di un sale neutro.

Nl.   **uitwisselingszuurgraad**
   Daling van de pH tengevolge van het toevoegen van een
   neutraal zout aan een grondsuspensie.

S.   **utbytesaciditet**
   Aciditet som uppkommer då en (helt eller delvis
   H^+-mättad) jord behandlas med ett neutralsalt.

Eng.   <u>hydrolytic acidity</u>
          Acidity produced by treating soil with a solution of a
          salt of a strong base and weak acid.

F.   <u>acidité hydrolytique</u>
          Acidité produite en traitant le sol avec une solution
          d'un sel de base forte et d'acide faible (généralement
          l'acétate de calcium) et résultant de l'échange entre
          le cation métallique du sel et les cations Hydrogène
          fixés par le complexe absorbant du sol.

D.   <u>hydrolytische Acidität</u>
          Fähigkeit saurer Böden, aus hydrolytisch spaltbaren
          Salzen (schwache Säure + starke Base) die Säure in
          Freiheit zu setzen.

Esp.   <u>acidez hidrolítica</u>
          Acidez producida al tratar un suelo con una solución de
          una sal derivada de una base fuerte y un ácido débil.

P.   <u>acidez hidrolítica</u>
          Acidez produzida quando se trata um solo com a solução
          de um sal resultante de uma base forte e um ácido fraco.

I.   <u>acidità (f) idrolitica</u>
          Acidità prodotta trattando un terreno con una soluzione
          di un sale con una base forte e un acido debole.

Nl.   ------------------------
          Zuurgraad verkregen door behandeling van de grond met
          een oplossing van een zout met een sterke base en zwak
          zuur.

S.   <u>hydrolytisk aciditet</u>
          Aciditet som uppkommer då en (helt eller delvis
          H^+-mättad) jord behandlas med ett salt av en stark
          bas och en svag syra.

Eng.   <u>absorbing complex</u>
> The whole absorbing material of the soil.

F.   <u>complexe absorbant</u>
> Ensemble des constituants du sol susceptibles
> d'absorber des éléments à partir d'une solution.

D.   <u>Sorptionskomplex</u> (m)
> Summe aller Sorptionsträger des Bodens.

Esp.   <u>complejo absorbente</u>
> Que retiene algo de la solución.

P.   <u>complexo de absorção</u>
> O que absorve qualquer coisa da solução.

I.   <u>complesso</u> (m) <u>d'assorbimento</u>
> Ciò che è capace di assorbire qualcosa da una
> soluzione.

Nl.   <u>absorptie complex</u>
> Het geheel van absorberende bestanddelen van de
> grond.

S.   <u>absorptionskomplex</u>
> Allt material i jorden med absorberande egenskaper.

Eng.   cation exchange
        Replacement of a surface valence-held cation by
        another.

F.   échange des cations
        Remplacement du cation x par y.

D.   Kationenumtausch (m)
        Ersatz eines durch Oberflächenkräfte festgehaltenen
        Kations durch ein anderes.

Esp.   intercambio de cationes
        Substitución del catión x per el cation y.

P.   troca de catiões
        Substituição do catião x por y.

I.   scambio di catione (m)
        Sostituzione di un catione x con uno y

Nl.   kationenwisseling
        Omwisseling van adsorptief gebonden kationen x
        door y.

S.   katjonutbyte
        Förträngning av katjon x med y.

Eng. exchangeable
      Describes ions capable of replacement in the absorbing
      complex.

F. échangeable
      Ions susceptibles d'être substitués dans le complexe
      absorbant.

D. austauschbar
      Bezeichnet Ionen die am Sorptionskomplex durch andere
      ersetzt werden können.

Esp. intercambiable
      Susceptible de ser substituido.

P. de troca
      Refere-se a iões capazes de serem substituidos no com-
      plexo de absorção.

I. scambiabile
      Capace di essere sostituito.

Nl. uitwisselbaar
      Geschikt om uit de geadsorbeerde toestand te worden
      verdrongen.

S. utbytbar
      Möjlig att utbyta.

Eng.   <u>exchange capacity</u>
        Milliequivalents of ions that can be absorbed by 100 g
        of material.

F.   <u>capacité d'échange</u>
        Nombre de milliéquivalents adsorbés par 100 gr de
        matériau dans des conditions de pH définies.

D.   <u>Sorptionskapazität</u> (f)
   <u>Umtauschkapazität</u> (f)
   <u>T-Wert</u> (m)
        Milliäquivalente von Ionen die pro 100 g Material
        sorbiert werden können.

Esp.   <u>capacidad de intercambio</u>
        Número de milieequivalentes que pueden ser absorbidos
        por 100 g de material.

P.   <u>capacidade de troca</u>
        Miliequivalentes de iões que podem ser absorvidos por
        100 gr de material.

I.   <u>capacità</u> (f) <u>di scambio</u>
        X milliequivalenti che possono essere assorbiti da
        100 g di materiale.

Nl.   <u>adsorptiecapaciteit</u>
        Milliequivalenten x, die kunnen worden geadsorbeerd
        per 100 gr materiaal.

S.   <u>utbyteskapacitet</u>
        M.e. x som kan absorberas per 100 g substans.

D18

Eng. base saturation
         Exchange capacity saturated with metallic cations at
         pH 7 or over.

F.   saturation en bases
         Etat du complexe correspondant à la rétention des
         cations dans des conditions déterminées.

D.   Basensättigung (f)
         Umtauschkapazität gesättigt mit Metallionen bei pH 7
         oder darüber.

Esp. saturación de bases
         El estado de retener la mayor cantidad posible de
         bases.

P.   saturação pelas bases
         O estado de retenção da maior quantidade possível de
         bases.

I.   saturazione (f) con basi
         Lo stato di ritenere la più gran quantità di basi.

Nl.   verzadiging met basen
         De toestand, waarbij de grootst mogelijke hoeveelheid
         base wordt vastgehouden.

S.   basmättning
         Ett tillstånd, då innehållet av utbytbara baser är
         maximalt.

Eng. degree of saturation (V)
 Percentage ratio of exchangeable cations without $H^+(=S)$
 to total exchangeable cations with $H^+(=T)$. $V = \dfrac{100S}{T}$.

F. degré de saturation (=V)
 Pourcentage du rapport des cations métalliques échange-
 ables à la somme de la totalité des cations échangeables
 (S) y compris les ions $H^+(T)$. $V = \dfrac{100S}{T}$.

D. Sättingungsgrad (m)
 V-Wert (m)
 %-Anteil der umtauschbaren Kationen ohne $H^+(S\text{-Wert})$ an
 der Summe der umtauschbaren Kationen einschliesslich
 $H^+(T\text{-Wert})$. $V = \dfrac{100S}{T}$.

Esp. porcentaje de saturación
 El tanto por ciento de la capacidad total de intercambio
 del complejo coloidal ocupado por cationes intercambiables.

P. grau de saturação
 percentagem de saturação
 Razão, em percentagem, entre o total de bases permu-
 táveis (valor S de Hissink) e a capacidade de troca de
 bases (valor T de Hissink).

I. grado (m) di saturazione (=V)
 Percentuale del rapporto dei cationi scambiabili senza
 $H^+(=S)$ e della somma dei cationi scambiabili con $H^+(=T)$;
 $V = \dfrac{100S}{T}$.

Nl. verzadigingsgraad
 De percentsgewijze verhouding van uitwisselbare basen
 zonder $H^+(=S)$ tot de som van uitwisselbare basen met
 $H^+(=T)$. $V = \dfrac{100S}{T}$.

S. basmättningsgrad
 Utbytbara metallkatjoner i procent av utbyteskapaciteten
 vid pH 7. $V = \dfrac{100S}{T}$.

D20

Eng.   **S value**
        Milliequivalents of exchangeable metallic cations in
        100 g of absorbing complex.

F.   **valeur S**
        Somme, exprimée en milliéq, des cations métalliques
        échangeables dans 100 gr de sol.

D.   **S-Wert** (m)
        In Milliäquivalenten angegebene Summe der austausch-
        baren Metallkationen eines Umtauschkorpers.

Esp.   **capacidad total de intercambio iónico**
        Miliequivalentes de cationes cambiables existentes en
        100 gr de complejo absorbente.

P.   **valor S**
        Miliequivalente de catiões metálicos de troca por 100 g
        de complexo de absorção.

I.   **valore** (m) **S**
        Somma, espressa in millieq, dei cationi metallici
        scambiabili nei 100 gr di complesso assorbente.

N.   **S-waarde**
        De in milliequivalenten uitgedrukte som der uitwissel-
        bare basen in 100 g adsorberende stof.

S.   **S-värde**
        Mängden utbytbara joner i m.e. per 100 gram av en
        jonbytare.

Eng. <u>depletion of bases</u>
Removal of exchangeable cations after displacement by H.

F. <u>entraînement (perte) des bases</u>
Entraînement des cations échangeables après déplacement par H.

D. <u>Entbasung</u> (f)
Entfernung austauschbarer Kationen nach Ersatz durch H.

Esp. <u>agotamiento de bases</u>
Remoción de cationes intercambiables después de su sustitución por H.

P. <u>dessaturação</u>
Substituição do Ca de troca, etc. por H.

I. <u>spostamento</u> (m) <u>delle basi</u> (f p)
Spostamento dei cationi scambiabili con l'H.

Nl. <u>ontkalking</u>
<u>verzuring, (basenverlies)</u>
Verdringing van uitwisselbare kationen door H.

S. <u>basutarmning</u>
Ersättande av baser med H^+.

Eng.   <u>nutrient</u>
        Substance required for plant growth.

F.   <u>élément nutritif</u>
        Substance absorbée par les racines des plantes.

D.   <u>Nährstoff</u> (m)
        Zur Ernährung der Pflanze notwendiger Stoff.

Esp.   <u>nutrimento</u>
        Substancia absorbida por las raíces de las plantas.

P.   <u>nutritivo</u>
        Substância absorvida pelas raizes das plantas.

I.   <u>sostanza</u> (f) <u>nutritizia</u>
        Sostanza assorbita dalle radici della pianta.

Nl.   **voedingsstof**
        Stof, die geabsorbeerd wordt door plantenwortels.

S.   <u>växtnäringsämne</u>
        Ämne som absorberas av växtrøtter.

Eng.   mineral reserve
             Plant-nutrient content of unweathered minerals in soil.

F.   réserve minérale
             Masse des éléments nutritifs minéraux présents dans le
             sol.

D.   Mineralreserve (f)
             Gehalt an unverwitterten Mineralen im Boden, die bei
             ihrer Verwitterung den Pflanzen Nährstoffe liefern
             können.

Esp.   reserva mineral
             Contenido de minerales no meteorizados en el suelo.

P.   reserva mineral
             Teor de substâncias minerais não meteorizadas no solo.

I.   riserva (f) minerale
             Contenuto di minerali nel terreno non alterati.

Nl.   minerale reserve
             Gehalte aan plantenvoedende stoffen aanwezig in onver-
             weerde mineralen van de grond.

S.   mineralförråd
             Jordens innehåll av ovittrade mineral.

D24

Eng. <u>available</u>
Capable of being taken up by plants at a rate significant to crop production.

F. <u>assimilable</u>
Susceptible d'être absorbé par les plantes.

D. <u>aufnehmbar</u>
Fähig, von den Pflanzenwurzeln aufgenommen zu werden.

Esp. <u>disponible</u>
<u>asimilable</u>
Capaz de ser absorbido por las raíces.

P. <u>assimilavel</u>
Capaz de ser absorvido pelas raizes.

I. <u>disponibile</u>
Capace di essere assorbito dall'apparato radicale.

Nl. <u>opneembaar</u>
Geschikt om door de wortels opgenomen te worden.

S. <u>tillgänglig</u>
Upptagbar för växtrötterna.

Eng. <u>fixation</u>

Conversion of a plant nutrient in the soil from a soluble or exchangeable form to a less soluble or non-exchange-able form.   (<u>See also</u> nitrogen fixation.)

F. <u>rétrogradation</u>

Passage à une forme moins assimilable d'un élément utilis-able par la plante.

D. <u>Festlegung</u> (f)

Überführung eines Pflanzennährstoffes in eine schwerer aufnehmbare Form.

Esp. <u>fijación</u>

Conversión en una forma inaprovechable.

P. <u>fixação</u>

Passagem a forma não assimilável.

I. <u>retrogradazione</u> (f)

Conversione di un elemento nutritivo delle piante in una forma meno assimilabile.

Nl. <u>fixatie</u>

Overgang naar een onopneembare vorm.

S. <u>fastläggning</u>
<u>fixering</u>

Omvandling till en svårtillgänglig form.

D26

Eng.   trace element
        minor element
            Nutrient required by plant in small amount.

F.   oligo-élément
            Elément nutritif indispensable aux plantes en très
            petite quantité.

D.   Spurenelement (n)
            Nährstoff mit sehr hohem Wirkungsfaktor, der für die
            Pflanzen wichtig ist, aber nur in sehr kleinen Mengen
            gebraucht wird.

Esp.   micro-elemento
        oligoelemento
            Elemento nutritivo esencial a la planta pero necesario
            en muy pequeñas cantidades.

P.   micronutriente
        oligoelemento
        elemento mínimo
        elemento vestigial
            Elemento essencial à planta mas necessário apenas em
            quantidades muito pequenas.

L.   elemento (m) micronutritivo
            Elemento fitogeno nutritivo essenziale alla pianta ma
            che viene richiesto in piccolissime quantità.

Nl.   sporenelement
            Voedingsstof, die nodig is voor de plant, maar die in
            zeer kleine hoeveelheid is vereist.

S.   mikroelement
            I mycket små mängder erforderligt men oumbärligt
            växtnäringsämne.

Eng. <u>foliar diagnosis</u>
>Estimation of plant-nutrient requirement based on analysis of leaves.

F. <u>diagnostic foliaire</u>
>Appréciation des conditions de nutrition minérale de la plante fondée sur l'analyse des feuilles.

D. <u>Blattanalyse</u> (f)
>Bestimmung des Pflanzennährstoffbedarfs auf Grund der Analyse von Blättern.

Esp. <u>diagnóstico foliar</u>
>Determinación de la necesidad de elementos nutritivos de las plantas basada en el análisis de las hojas.

P. <u>diagnostico pelhas folhas</u>
>Estimativa da necessidade em elementos nutritivos baseada na análise das folhas.

I. <u>diagnosi</u> (f) <u>del tessuto</u> (m) <u>foliare</u>
>Diagnosi delle esigenze di elementi nutritizi fondato sull'analisi delle foglie.

Nl. <u>bladweefsel diagnose</u>
>Schatting van de voedingstoestand van de plant en grond, gebaseerd op bladanalyse.

S. <u>bladanalys</u>
>Uppskattning av växtnäringsbehov med ledning av kemisk analys på bladen.

Section E

ORGANIC MATTER, HUMUS

MATIERES ORGANIQUES, HUMUS

MATERIA ORGANICA, HUMUS

Eng. litter
      Leaves and other undecomposed residues lying on the
      soil.

F. litière du sol
      Feuilles, et débris organiques en voie de décomposi-
      tion, recouvrant le sol.

D. Streuschicht (f)
      Blätter und andere unzersetzte organische Materialen
      die den Boden bedecken.

Esp. hojarasca
      Hojas, etc. caidas sobre el suelo.

P. manta morta
      Folhas, etc. jazendo no solo.

I. copertura (f) morta del terreno
      Foglie, rami ecc. indecomposti che sono sparsi sul
      terreno.

Nl. strooisel (laag)
      Bladeren enz. die op de grond liggen.

S. förna
      Löv etc. som kvarligger på marken.

E2

Eng. <u>muck</u>
        Partially decomposed organic matter, plant remains not
        discernible, accumulated in a wet place and mixed with
        some mineral matter.

F.   ----------
        Matière organique en décomposition, accumulée en un
        lieu humide et melangée à des matières minérales.

D.   ----------
        Zersetzte, an einem feuchten Ort angehäufte organische
        Substanz, vermischt mit etwas mineralischer Substanz.

Esp. <u>barro turboso</u>
        Materia orgánica descompuesta, acumulada en lugares
        húmedos y mezclada con algo de materia mineral.

P.   <u>solo turfoso</u>
        Matéria orgânica acumulada em condições de má drenagem
        e misturada com alguma matéria mineral.

I.   <u>fango</u> (m) <u>organico</u>
        Materia organica decomposta, accumulatasi in una
        località umida, mescolata con materiali minerali.

Nl. <u>meermolm</u>
        Verslagen organische stof, op de bodem van een meer
        opgehoopt, gemengd met wat minerale stof.

S.   <u>dyjord</u>
        Jord i huvudsak bildad genom utflockning av kolloidala
        humusämnen.

Eng. duff (U.S.)
      raw humus (U.K.)
         Surface horizon of partly decomposed organic remains
         resting on mineral soil.

F.   couverture organique
         Horizon superficiel formé de matière organique peu
         décomposée.

D.   Rohhumus (m)
         Vom Mineralboden scharf abgegrenzte in Zersetzung
         begriffene verfilzte Streuschicht von saurer Reaktion
         (Humussäuren).

Esp. mantillo
         Un horizonte superficial de materia organica descan-
         sando sobre un suelo mineral.

P.   camada humífera
         Um horizonte superficial orgânico que consiste numa
         camada emaranhada de matéria orgânica turfosa,
         apenas ligeiramente decomposta, assente no solo
         mineral (horizonte A_o).

I.   umus (m) bruto (grezzo)
         Un orizzonte organico superficiale che riposa sotto
         la copertura morta e sopra terreno minerale.

Nl.   bosturf
         Een horizont van weinig gedisintegreerde organische
         stof, opgehoopt op de minerale grond.

S.   råhumus(-täcke)
         Ett organiskt ytskikt av sur karaktär vilande på
         mineraljord.

E4

Eng. <u>mor</u>
  <u>raw humus</u>
   A_O horizon unmixed with and sharply demarcated from
   the underlying mineral horizon. Consists of L, F
   and H horizons.

F.   <u>humus brut</u>
   Matière organique grossière peu decomposée, de
   réaction fortement acide.

D.   <u>Auflagehumus</u> (m)
   Aus Rohhumus bestehender A_O-Horizont (des Podsol-
   bodens) der sich scharf vom darunterliegenden
   Mineralboden abhebt.

Esp. <u>humus ácido</u>
   Materia orgánica ácida del suelo forestal, que tiene
   la capa superior F y la inferior H.

P.   <u>húmus ácido (cru)</u>
   Matéria orgânica ácida dos solos florestais com a
   camada F superiormente e a camada H inferiormente.

I.   <u>orizzonte</u> (m) <u>a umus</u> (m) <u>acido</u>
   Orizzonte A_O di residui organici arruffati e intrec-
   ciati, demarcato chiaramente dal sottostante orizzonte
   minerale.

Nl. <u>zure humus</u>
   Zure, organische stof van bosgrond, die een bovenste
   F-horizont en een onderste H-horizont heeft.

S.   <u>råhumus</u>
   Sur organisk substans i skogsjord med ett övre F-skikt
   och ett nedre H-skikt.

Eng. __mull__
__mild humus__
Forest-humus layer of mixed organic and mineral matter
with a gradual transition to the underlying mineral
horizon.

F. __humus doux__
Matière organique bien décomposée, de réaction moyennement acide ou neutre.

D. __Mull__ (m)
Mit mineralischen Teilchen vermischter, milder und
krümeliger Humus, in dem die Ausgangsstoffe durch die
Tätigkeit der Bodenorganismen weitgehend umgesetzt sind.

Esp. __humus dulce__
Capa superior orgánica y mineral, debilmente ácida o
neutra, del suelo forestal.

P. __húmus doce__
Matéria orgânica e mineral da camada superior do solo
florestal, ligeiramente ácida ou neutra.

I. __umus__ (m) __saturo glomerulare forestale__
Strato superiore del terreno forestale leggermente
acido o neutro, contenente parti organiche e minerali.

Nl. __milde humus__
Zwak zure of neutrale, humeuze en met minerale gronde
gemengde bovenlaag van bosgrond.

S. __mull__
Svagt sur eller neutral, väl förmultnad vanligen
mineralblandad, organisk substans.

119

E6

Eng. ------------
          Transition between raw humus and mull.

F. ------------
          Type d'humus acide, intermédiaire entre l'humus brut
          et le mull.

D.   Moder (m)
          Lockere, meist saure Humusform aus mehr oder weniger
          zersetzten Pflanzenresten.

Esp. ------------
          Transición entre humus ácido y humus dulce.

P. ------------
          Transição entre húmus ácido e húmus doce.

I. ------------
          Tipo di umus acido, che sta in mezzo all'umus immaturo
          e a quello maturo (mull).

Nl.   bosmolm
          Reeds ver (half) vergane strooisellaag in bossen, of
          ver vergaan bosveen (min of meer de A_0-laag uit het
          gepodzoleerde ABC-profiel, althans de hogere lagen
          ervan).

S.   mår
          Övergångsform mellan råhumus och mull.

Eng. <u>humification</u>
        Transformation of organic matter into humus.

F. <u>humification</u>
        Evolution de la matière organique dans le sol,
        tendant à donner des acides humiques et humines.

D. <u>Humifizierung</u>
        Abbau und Umwandlung der organischen Substanz
        im Boden und Bildung von Huminstoffen.

Esp. <u>humificación</u>
        La descomposición de la materia orgánica en el
        suelo.

P. <u>humificação</u>
        Decomposição da matéria orgânica no solo,
        formando húmus.

I. <u>umificazione</u> (f)
        Il disfacimento della materia organica entro il
        terreno.

Nl. <u>humusvorming</u>
        Omzetting van organische stof in de grond tot
        min of meer resistente stikstofhoudende verbind-
        ingen.

S. <u>humifiering</u>
   <u>förmultning</u>
        Partiell nedbrytning och omvandling av organisk
        substans i jorden.

E8

Eng.   humus
              The amorphous (colloidal) organic matter of soil (U.K.).
              The organic complex of the soil which is more or less
              résistant to microbial decomposition (U.S.).

F.   humus
              Matière organique évoluée assez résistante à une décom-
              position ultérieure.

D.   Humus (m), (Gesamthumus) (m)
              Gesamtheit der (in Ab-, Um- und Aufbau begriffenen)
              organischen Substanz des Bodens.

Esp.   humus
              Materia orgánica parcialmente descompuesta y que
              resiste una descomposición ulterior.

P.   húmus
              Matéria orgânica do solo bem decomposta e mais ou menos
              estável.

I.   umus (m), humus (m)
              Materia organica parzialmente decomposta e che resiste
              e successive decomposizioni.

Nl.   humus
              Organische stof, gedeeltelijk afgebroken en weerstand
              biedend aan verdere afbraak.

S.   humus
              Organisk substans delvis nedbruten och omvandlad samt
              relativt motståndskraftig mot vidare sönderdelning.

Eng. humic acid
   Organic matter extractable from soil by alkali and
   precipitated by acid.

F. acide humique
   Fraction de la matière organique du sol extractible
   par les bases et précipitable par les acides.

D. Huminsäuren (f p)
   Alkalilöslischer und säurefallbarer Anteil der Huminstoffe.

Esp. ácido húmico
   Materia orgánica extraíble del suelo por medio de
   alcalis y precipitada por ácidos.

P. ácido húmico
   Matéria orgânica que se extrai do solo por meio de
   álcalis e precipita pelos ácidos.

I. acido (m) umico
   Materia organica estraibile dal terreno per mezzo
   di alcali e precipitata con acido.

Nl. huminezuur
   Organische stof, die oplosbaar is in alkali en
   neergeslagen wordt door zuur.

S. humussyra
   Organiskt material som kan extraheras ur jord med
   alkali och utfällas med syra.

Eng.   <u>fulvic acid</u>
          The alkali-soluble fraction of humus not precipitated
          by acid.

F.   <u>acide fulvique</u>
          Fraction de l'acide humique soluble à l'eau.

D.   <u>Fulvosäuren</u> (f p)
          Alkalilöslicher, durch Säure nicht fällbarer Anteil
          der Huminstoffe von gelb-roter Farbe.

Esp.   <u>ácido fúlvico</u>
          La fracción del ácido húmico soluble en agua.

P.   <u>ácido fúlvico</u>
          Parte do húmus que é solúvel na água.

I.   <u>acido</u> (m) <u>fulvico</u>
          La frazione solubile in acqua dell'acido umico.

Nl.   <u>fulvozuur</u>
          Het in water oplosbare gedeelte der humuszuren.

S.   <u>fulvosyra</u>
          Den vattenlösliga delen av humussyra.

Eng.   hymatomelanic acid
        The alcohol-soluble fraction of humic acid.

F.   acide hymatomélanique
        Fraction de l'acide humique soluble dans l'alcool.

D.   Hymatomelansäuren (f p)
        Alkohollösliche Fraktion der Huminsäure.

Esp.   ácido himatomelánico
        La fracción del ácido húmico soluble en alcohol.

P.   ácido himatomelânico
        Fracção do ácido húmico solúvel no álcool.

I.   acido (m) imatomelanico
        La frazione solubile in alcool dell'acido umico.

Nl.   hymatomelaanzuur
        Het in alcohol oplosbare gedeelte van huminezuur.

S.   hymatomelansyra
        Den alkohollösliga delen av humussyra.

Eng.　<u>humin</u>
　　　　The alkali-insoluble fraction of humus.

F.　　<u>humine</u>
　　　　Fraction la moins soluble des matières organiques
　　　　du sol.　Correspond approximativement à l'insoluble
　　　　au bromure d'acétyle et aux alcalis après lavage
　　　　aux acides dilués.

D.　　<u>Humine</u> (n p)
　　　　Nur in heisser Natronlauge löslicher Anteil der
　　　　Huminstoffe.

Esp.　<u>humina</u>
　　　　La fracción del humo insoluble en alcalis.

P.　　<u>humina</u>
　　　　Fracção do húmus que é insolúvel nos álcalis.

I.　　<u>umina</u> (f)
　　　　La frazione dell'umus insolubile in alcali.

Nl.　　<u>humine</u>
　　　　Het in alkali onoplosbare deel van de humus.

S.　　<u>humín</u>
　　　　Organiskt material i jord som inte kan extraheras
　　　　med alkali.

Eng.   "brown humic acid"
          Red-brown form of humic acid, less readily flocculated
          and poorer in nitrogen than "gray humic acid."

F.   -------------------
          Type d'acide humique rouge-brun, de floculation moins
          aisée et d'un taux d'azote moins élevé que dans les
          acides humiques gris.

D.   Braunhuminsäuren (f p)
          Huminsäuretyp von rötlich-brauner Farbe, der schwerer
          fällbar und meist N-armer ist als die Grauhuminsäure.

Esp.   "ácido húmico pardo"
          Forma castaño rojiza del ácido húmico, menos facilmente
          floculable y más pobre en nitrógeno que el "ácido húmico
          gris."

P.   "ácido húmico pardo"
          Forma pardo avermelhada do ácido húmico que flocula mais
          dificilmente e é mais pobre em azote do que o "acido
          húmico cinzento."

I.   acido (m) umico bruno
          Acido umico rosso-bruno, di coagulazione meno facile e
          di contenuto d'azoto meno elevato che negli'acidi umici
          grigi.

Nl.   bruin huminezuur
          Een roodbruine vorm van huminezuur dat minder gemakke-
          lijk uitvlokt en armer is aan stikstof dan grijs humine-
          zuur.

S.   -------------------
          Rödbrun humussyra.

Eng. "gray humic acid"
       Gray, easily flocculated, nitrogen-rich form of humic
       acid, characteristic of chernozems.

F.   ------------------
       Type d'acide humique gris caractéristique aux cherno-
       zems, de floculation plus aisée et d'un taux d'azote
       plus élevé que dans les acides humiques bruns.

D.   Grauhuminsäuren (f p)
       Für Schwarzerdehumus charakteristischer grauer Humin-
       säuretyp, der leichter flockbar und meist N-reicher ist
       als die Braunhuminsäure.

Esp. "ácido húmico gris"
       Forma del ácido húmico característica de los suelos
       chernozem, de color gris, facilmente floculable y
       rico en nitrógeno.

P.   "ácido húmico cinzento"
       Forma do ácido húmico de côr cinzenta, que flocula
       com facilidade, rica em azote, característica dos
       chernozems.

I.   acido (m) umico grigio
       Tipo d'acido umico grigio caratteristico dei cerno-
       zems, di coagulazione più facile e di contenuto
       d'azoto più elevato che negli acidi umici bruni.

Nl.   grijs humusrijk zuur
       Een grijze vorm van humus zuur, rijk aan stikstof,
       hetwelk gemakkelijk uitvlokt en karakteristiek is
       voor chernozems.

S.   --------------------
       Mörkgråa humussyror.

Eng. "stable humus"
   The part of humus that is resistant to microbial
   attack (and is insoluble in acetyl bromide).

F.   humus stable (ou simplement humus)
   Partie de la matière organique du sol résistante
   à la décomposition par voie microbienne.

D.   Dauerhumus
   Biologisch schwer zersetzbarer Anteil der organischen
   Substanz des Bodens (etwa gleich der Acetyl-bromid-
   unlöslichen Fraktion und dem Begriff "Huminstoffe").

Esp. "humus estable"
   Parte del humus resistente a la acción microbiana e
   insoluble en bromuro de acetilo.

P.   húmus estável
   A parte do húmus que não é atacada pelos micro-
   organismos.

I.   umus (m) stabile
   La parte di umus che è resistente agli attacchi dei
   microbi.

Nl. stabiele humus
   Gedeelte van de humus, dat in hoge mate bestand is
   tegen microbiologische afbraak.

S.   "Dauerhumus"
   Den del av den organiska substansen i jorden som är
   motståndskraftig mot mikrobiell nedbrytning (den
   humusfraktion som är olöslig i acetylbromid).

E16

Eng. <u>"unstable humus"</u>
  Readily decomposable part of humus, corresponding
  approximately to that soluble in 80% sulphuric acid.

F. ----------------

D. <u>Nährhumus</u> (m)
  Biologisch leicht umsetzbarer Anteil der organischen
  Substanz des Bodens, etwa gleich der in 80%er Schwefel-
  säure löslichen Fraktion.

Esp. <u>"humus inestable"</u>
  Fracción del humus que se descompone facilmente.
  Corresponde aproximadamente a la que se disuelve
  en ácido sulfúrico al 80%.

P. <u>húmus nutriente</u>
  Fracção do húmus que fàcilmente se decompõe e que
  corresponde aproximadamente à parte solúvel em
  ácido sulfúrico a 80%.

I. <u>umus</u> (m) <u>nutritivo</u>
  Parte prontamente decomponibile dell'umus, corrispondente approssimativamente a quella solubile in
  acido solforico all'80%.

Nl. <u>vlottende (instabiele) humus</u>
  Gedeelte van de organische stof in de grond, dat
  geschikt is voor snelle microbiologische afbraak.

S. <u>närhumus</u>
  Lätt nedbrytbar organisk substans i jorden, approxi-
  mativt motsvarande den del som löses i 80% H_2SO_4.

Eng. ------------------------
Red-brown intermediate product formed during humification of lignin and having characteristics similar to
fulvic acid.

F. ------------------------
Produit intermédiaire rouge-brun, se formant lors de
l'humification des lignines et possédant un caractère
analogue à l'acide fulvique.

D. <u>Humoligninsäuren (f p)</u>
Bei der Humifizierung von Lignin auftretende rotbraune
Zwischenprodukte, die ähnliche Eigenschaften wie die
Fulvosäure besitzen.

Esp. ------------------------
Producto intermedio, de color castaño rojizo, formado
durante la humificación de la lignina, de propiedades
análogas al ácido fúlvico.

P. ------------------------
Produto intermediário pardo-vermelho formado durante
a humificação da linhina, com características semelhantes ás do ácido fúlvico.

I. ------------------------
Prodotto intermedio di colore rosso-bruno, formantosi
durante l'umificazione della lignina e presentando
caratteristiche come l'acido fulvico.

Nl. ------------------------
Eon roodbruin tussenproduct ontstaan gedurende de humus-
vorming, waarvan de eigenschappen overeenkomst vertonen
met fulvozuren. Zij worden niet neergeslagen door an-
organische zuren.

S. ------------------------
Rödbruna humusämnen, bildade vid humifiering av trä,
om vilka man antar, att de utgör en mellanprodukt
mellan lignin och humussyror.

Eng. ------------------
The humin fraction insoluble in hot alkali.

F. ------------------
Fraction renfermant l'humine insoluble dans
les alcalis à chaud.

D. <u>Humuskohle</u> (f)
In heisser NaOH unlöslicher Anteil der Huminstoffe.

Esp. ------------------
La fracción húmica insoluble en alcalí caliente.

P. ------------------
A fracção humina insolúvel nos álcalis a quente.

I. ------------------
Frazione dell'umina insolubile in alcali caldo.

Nl. ------------------
De in hete loog onoplosbare humus fractie.

S. ------------------
Den i varm NaOH olösliga humusämnesfraktionen.

Eng. ------------------
Corresponds approximately to "stable humus."

F. ------------------
Matières organiques foncées, produites dans le
sol par humification et correspondant à peu près
à l'humus stable.

D. __Huminstoffe__ (m p)
Durch Humifizierung (richtiger "Huminifizierung")
entstandene dunkelgefärbte organische Stoffe im
Boden (entspricht etwa dem ackerbaulichen Begriff
"Dauerhumus").

Esp. ------------------

P. ------------------
Corresponde aproximadamente ao "húmus estável."

I. ------------------
Sostanze organiche di colore scuro, prodotte nel
suolo per mezzo d'umificazione; all'incirca umus
stabile.

Nl. ------------------
Komt ongeveer overeen met duurzame (stabiele)
humus.

S. __humusämnen__
Genom humifiering bildade mörkfärgade organiska
ämnen i marken (motsvarar i stort sett termen
dauerhumus).

E20

Eng. ------------------------
Humic matter excluding "huminstoffe."

F. ------------------------
Totalité des matières humiques, à l'exclusion
de l'"huminstoffe."

D. <u>Nichthuminstoffe</u> (m p)
Gesamthumus minus Huminstoffe (hierunter fällt
der "Nährhumus").

Esp. ------------------------
Totalidad de la materia orgánica menos el humus.

P. ------------------------
Matéria húmica com exclusão da "huminstoffe."

I. ------------------------
Totalità della sostanze umiche, le materie delle
"huminstoffe" non comprese.

Nl. ------------------------
Humus materiaal zonder "huminstoffen."

S. ------------------------
Total organisk substans minus humusämnen.

BIOLOGY, ECOLOGY

BIOLOGIE, ECOLOGIE

BIOLOGIA, ECOLOGIA

Eng. <u>edaphon</u>
     The whole living community of the soil.

F. ----------
     Totalité des organismes vivants dans le sol.

D. <u>Edaphon</u> (n)
     Die Bodenlebewelt.

Esp. <u>edafón</u>
     La comunidad viviente del suelo considerada en
     conjunto.

P. "<u>edaphon</u>"
     Toda a comunidade viva do solo.

I. -----------
     La totalità degli organismi viventi nel suolo.

Nl. <u>edaphon</u>
     De volledige levende bodemgemeenschap.

S. <u>edafon</u>
     Kollektivbeteckning på markens organismvärld.

F2

Eng. indicator plants
        Plants which commonly grow where particular soil
        conditions prevail.

F. plantes indicatrices
        Plantes caractéristiques de conditions parti-
        culières de sol.

D. Zeigerpflanzen (f p)
    Leitpflanzen (f p)
        Pflanzen, die für besondere Bodenzustände typisch
        sind.

Esp. plantas indicadoras
        Plantas típicas que revelan condiciones especiales
        del suelo.

P. plantas indicadoras
        Plantas típicas de certas condições especiais do
        solo.

I. piante (f p) indicatrici
        Piante tipiche di particolari condizioni del suolo.

Nl. indicator planten
        Planten, die kenmerkend zijn voor bepaalde bodem-
        toestanden.

S. indikatorväxter
        Växter typiska för vissa förhållanden i jorden.

Eng. <u>nodule bacteria</u>
> Nitrogen-fixing micro-organisms of genus <u>Rhizobium</u>
> living in nodules on roots of legumes, and also in
> the soil.

F. <u>bactéries des nodosités</u>
> Microorganismes fixateurs d'azote vivant sur les
> racines des légumineuses.

D. <u>Knöllchenbakterien</u> (n)
> In den Wurzelverdickungen (Knöllchen) der Leguminosen
> lebende, N-bindende Mikroorganismen.

Esp. <u>bacterias nodulares</u>
> Microorganismos que viven en las raíces de las legumi-
> nosas.

P. <u>bacterias dos nodulos</u>
> Microorganismos existentes nas raizes das leguminosas.

I. <u>batteri</u> (m p) <u>dei tuberculi</u> (m p) <u>radicali</u>
> Microorganismi che vivono nei nodoli delle radici delle
> leguminose che fissano l'azoto.

Nl. <u>knolletjes bacteriën</u>
> Stikstof bindende bacteriën levend in knolletjes op de
> wortels van leguminosen.

S. <u>baljväxt-bakterier</u>
<u>knölbakterier</u>
> Kvävebindende mikroorganismer som leva i baljväxternas
> rotknölar.

Eng. **mycorrhiza**
> Symbiotic association of fungi and roots.

F. **mycorrhises**
> Filaments mycéliens vivant en symbiose avec les racines.

D. **Mykorrhiza** (f)
> Symbiose von Pilzen mit den Wurzeln höheren Pflanzen (Waldbäume, Orchideen).

Esp. **micorriza**
> Hilos formados por hongos dentro de las raíces.

P. **micorriza**
> Associação simbiótica entre certos fungos do solo e as raizes das plantas.

I. **micorizza**
> Filamenti formati da funghi entro le radici.

Nl. **mycorrhiza**
> Wortelschimmels die in symbiose met de plant leven.

S. **mykorrhiza**
> Symbiotisk sammenlevnad av svampar och rötter.

Eng. mineralization
>   Release of mineral matter from organic combination by
>   microbial decomposition.

F. minéralisation
>   Libération de la matière minérale par décomposition
>   microbiologique des substances organiques.

D. Mineralisierung (f)
>   Mineralisation (f)
>   Freilegung organisch festgelegter Mineralstoffe durch
>   mikrobiellen Abbau der organischen Substanz.

Esp. mineralización
>   Liberación de la fracción de materia mineral contenida
>   en los compuestos orgánicos por efecto de la actividad
>   de los microorganismos del suelo.

P. mineralização
>   Libertação de matéria mineral das combinações orgânicas
>   por decomposição microbiana.

I. mineralizzazione (f)
>   Liberazione della sostanza minerale per decomposizione
>   microbiologica da combinazioni organiche.

Nl. mineralisatie
>   Het vrijkomen van minerale bestanddelen uit de organische
>   verbindingen door microbiologische afbraak.

S. mineralisering
>   Frigörelse av organiska beståndsdelar vid mikrobiell
>   nedbrytning av org. materiel.

F6

Eng. <u>nitrification</u>
>Biological oxidation of nitrogen to nitrate.

F. <u>nitrification</u>
>Oxydation de l'azote ammoniacal donnant naissance
à des nitrates.

D. <u>Nitrifikation</u>
>Oxydation von Ammoniak zu Nitrat durch mikrobielle
Tätigkeit.

Esp. <u>nitrificación</u>
>Oxidation biológica del material nitrogenado para
formar nitrato.

P. <u>nitrificação</u>
>Oxidação da matéria azotada para formar nitratos.

I. <u>nitrificazione</u> (f)
>Ossidazione di materiali azotati per formare il
nitrato.

Nl. <u>nitrificatie</u>
>Oxydatie van ammoniak-stikstof tot nitraat.

S. <u>nitrifikation</u>
>Oxidation av ammoniakkväve till nitrat.

Eng. ammonification
       Microbiological transformation of nitrogenous
       compounds to ammonia nitrogen.

F.   ammonisation
       Transformation microbiologique des composés
       azotés organiques en azote ammoniacal.

D.   Ammonifikation
       Mikrobiologische Umwandlung N-haltiger Stoffe
       in Ammoniakstickstoff.

Esp. amonificación
       Transformación microbiológica de compuestos
       aminados en nitrógeno amoniacal.

P.   amonificação
       Transformação microbiológica dos compostos
       amínicos em azoto amoniacal.

I.   ammonificazione (f)
       Trasformazione microbiologica dei composti
       d'amine in azoto ammoniacale.

Nl.   ammonificatie
       Omzetting van aminoverbindingen door microben
       in ammoniak-stikstof.

S.   ammonifikation
       Mikrobiologisk nedbrytning av kvävehaltiga
       organiska föreningar till ammoniak-kväve.

F8

Eng. "aminization"
Microbiological decomposition of protein to
amino compounds.

F. ------------
Décomposition microbiologique des protéines en
composés aminés.

D. Aminobildung
Mikrobiologische Umwandlung von N-haltigen
Verbindungen in Aminostoffe.

Esp. aminación
Transformación microbiológica de las proteínas
en compuestos aminados.

P. ------------
Decomposição microbiológica das proteínas em
aminas.

I. aminizzazione (f)
Decomposizione microbiologica delle proteine in
composti d'amine.

Nl. aminizatie
Ontleding van eiwitten door microben in amino-
verbindingen.

S. ------------
Mikrobiologisk nerbrytning av proteiner till
aminoföreningar.

Eng. nitrogen fixation
          Conversion of atmospheric nitrogen to a combined
          form.

F. fixation de l'azote
          Passage de l'azote atmosphérique à une forme
          combinée.

D. Stickstoffbindung (f)
          Umwandlung von atmosphärischem Stickstoff in
          gebundene Form.

Esp. fijación de nitrógeno
          Transformación del nitrógeno atmósferico por los
          microorganismos.

P. fixação do azoto
          Combinação do azoto atmosferico provocada por
          microorganismos específicos.

I. azotofissazione (f)
    induzione (f) dell'azoto (m)
          La trasformazione di azoto atmosferico dovuta ai
          microrganismi in una forma combinata.

Nl. stikstofvastlegging
     stikstofbinding
          Omzetting van luchtstikstof door micro-organismen
          in organische vorm.

S. kvävefixering
          Överföring av atmosfäriskt kväve till kemiskt
          bundet kväve.

F10

Eng. <u>denitrification</u>
Reduction of nitrate or nitrite; reduction to nitrogen.

F. <u>dénitrification</u>
Réduction des nitrates.

D. <u>Denitrifikation</u> (f)
Reduktion von Nitraten zu elementarem Stickstoff durch mikrobielle Tätigkeit.

Esp. <u>desnitrificación</u>
Reducción de los nitratos.

P. <u>desnitrificação</u>
Redução dos nitratos.

I. <u>denitrificazione</u> (f)
Riduzione del nitrato.

Nl. <u>denitrificatie</u>
Reductie van nitraat tot stikstof in gasform (stikstof en stikstof-oxydule).

S. <u>denitrifikation</u>
Reduktion av nitrat eller nitrit till fritt kväve.

146

Eng. ----------------------------
         (1) Degree of decomposition of plant residues in peat
         soils.
         (2) Proportion of acetyl-bromide-insoluble material
         in soil organic matter.

F.   degré de décomposition
         (1) Degré de décomposition des résidus végétaux dans
         les sols tourbeux.
         (2) Le taux dans le sol des matières organiques in-
         solubles dans le bromure d'acétyle.

D.   Zersetzungsgrad (m)
         (1) Bei der Moorcharakterizierung— wie weit das
         pflanzliche Ausgangsmaterial umgewandelt ist.
         (2) Gehalt der organischen Substanz des Bodens an
         azetylbromidunlöslichen Huminstoffen (nach Springer).

Esp. ----------------------------
         Grado de descomposición de los residuos vegetales.

P.   ----------------------------
         Grau de decomposição dos restos vegetais.

I.   ----------------------------
         (1) Grado di decomposizione dei residui vegetali nei
         terreni torbosi.
         (2) Contenuto nel suolo delle sostanze organiche in-
         solubili nel bromuro d'acetile.

Nl.   verweringsgraad
         Mate waarin het organische materiaal is omgezet.

S.   förmultningsgrad
         Anger hur långt det ursprungliga materialets förmult-
         ning fortskridit i torvjordar. (Avser även den
         organiska substansens halt av azetylbromidolösliga
         beståndsdelar.)

147

Section G

CULTIVATION, MANURING, FERTILITY

CULTURE, FUMURE, FERTILITE

CULTIVO, ABONO ORGANICO, FERTILIDAD

Eng. <u>fallow</u>
　　　　Condition of soil left without crop for a time.

F. <u>jachère</u>
　　　　Etat du sol laissé sans culture pendant un certain
　　　　temps.

D. <u>brach</u>
　　　　Zustand des Ackers, der eine Zeit lang unbebaut
　　　　liegen bleibt.

Esp. <u>barbecho</u>
　　　　Práctica consistente en dejar el suelo sin cultivo
　　　　por algún tiempo.

P. <u>pousio</u>
　　　　Estado do solo que não é cultivado durante algum
　　　　tempo.

I. <u>maggese</u> (m)
　　　　Condizione del suolo per cui vien lasciato senza
　　　　culture per un certo periodo di tempo. (Si usa
　　　　la parola maggese se il riposo dura almeno un
　　　　ciclo vegetativo di una cultura della ruotazione.)

Nl. <u>braak</u>
　　　　De toestand van de grond, waarop gedurende een
　　　　zekere tijd geen gewas verbouwd wordt.

S. <u>i träda</u>
　　　　Tillstånd hos åkerjord som under en vegetations-
　　　　period eller del därav hålles obeväxt.

Eng. <u>strip cropping</u>
Practice of growing crops in strips along contours or across prevailing direction of wind.

F. <u>culture en bandes</u>
Pratique consistant à effectuer des cultures en bandes parallèles aux courbes de niveau ou normales à la direction la plus fréquente du vent.

D. <u>Streifenkultur</u>
Anlage der Kulturen in Streifen entlang den Höhenlinien oder quer zur Hauptwindrichtung.

Esp. <u>cultivo en fajas</u>
Práctica consistente en sembrar en fajas a lo largo de las curvas de nivel o perpendicularmente a la dirección de los vientos dominantes.

P. <u>culturas em faixas</u>
Disposição das culturas em faixas alternadas segundo as curvas de nível ou perpendicularmente á direcção dos ventos dominantes.

I. <u>coltivazione (f) a striscie</u>
Pratica agronomica di disporre le culture in striscie lungo le **curve** di livello o perpendicolarmente al vento predominante.

Nl. <u>teelt in stroken</u>
Teelt van gewassen in stroken langs de hoogtelijnen of dwars op de overheersende windrichting.

S. <u>odling i band, (strip cropping)</u>
Grödor odlas i remsor eller band längs nivålinjer eller vinkelrätt mot förhärskande vindriktning.

Eng.   <u>dry farming</u>
>   The practice of crop production, without irrigation,
>   where rainfall is deficient.

F.   <u>culture sèche, (culture des pays secs)</u>
>   Pratique culturale sans irrigation des régions où la
>   pluviosité est déficiente.

D.   <u>Trockenlandwirtschaft</u> (f), (<u>dry farming</u>)
>   Praxis des Pflanzenbaus in regenarmen Gebieten.

Esp.   <u>cultivo de secano</u>
>   La práctica de producción de cultivos donde las
>   lluvias son deficientes.

P.   <u>cultivo de sequeiro</u>
>   A lavoura das regiões de chuva deficiente.

I.   <u>aridocoltura</u> (f)
>   La produzione di culture dove le precipitazioni non
>   sono sufficienti senza irrigazione.

Nl.   <u>dry farming</u>
>   De teelt van landbouwgewassen in streken waar een
>   regentekort heerst.

S.   <u>dry farming</u>
>   Metod för växtodling i regnfattiga trakter.

Eng. <u>mellow</u>
Porous, softer than friable, without tendency to become compact.

F. <u>meuble</u>
Poreux, plus tendre que friable, sans tendance à devenir compact.

D. <u>gar</u>
Im Zustand der Gare.

Esp. <u>mullido</u>
Poroso, más blando que friable, sin tendencia a volverse compacto.

P. <u>brando</u>
Poroso, mais macio de que freável, sem tendencia para se tornar compacto.

I. <u>morbido</u>
<u>polposo</u>
<u>pastoso</u>
Poroso, più soffice che friabile, senza che abbia la tendenza a diventar compatto.

Nl. <u>zacht</u>
Poreus, zachter dan los, zonder neiging compact te worden.

S. <u>lucker</u>
Porös och utan benägenhet för att bli kompakt.

Eng. <u>mellowness</u>
>   The optimal physical, chemical and biological condition
>   for plant growth.

F.   <u>-----------</u>
>   Condition physique, chimique et biologique du sol la
>   plus favorable au développement des plantes, carac-
>   térisée par une stabilité de la structure grumeleuse.

D.   <u>Gare</u> (f)
>   Das Ziel der Bodenbearbeitung; der günstigste physika-
>   lische, chemische und biologische Bodenzustand, der
>   ein optimales Pflanzenwachstum ermöglicht. Die Gare
>   ist die Summe der Wirkung kolloid-chemischer und mikro-
>   biologischer Einzelvorgänge. Ihr Kennzeichnen ist die
>   Beständigkeit der Krumelstruktur.

Esp. <u>sazón</u>
      <u>tempero</u>
>   La condición óptima del suelo para el crecimiento
>   vegetal, considerado como en un triple aspecto:
>   físico, químico y biológico.

P.   <u>sazão óptima</u>
>   Condição física, química e biológica do solo óptima
>   para o desenvolvimento das plantas.

I.   <u>tempera</u> (f)
>   Condizione fisica, chimica et biologica del suolo la
>   più favorevole allo sviluppo delle piante, caratteriz-
>   zata per una stabilità dalla struttura grumosa.

Nl.   <u>rijpheid</u>
>   De voor den plantengroei optimale natuurkundige,
>   chemische en biologische toestand van de grond.

S.   <u>-----------</u>
>   Optimala, fysikaliska, kemiska och biologiska för-
>   hållanden i den odlade jorden. Jordbearbetnings
>   ändamål.

Eng. <u>tilth</u>
State of aggregation of soil in relation to its
response to cultivation implements.

F. <u>état d'ameublissement</u>
Etat de la structure correspondant à une plus ou
moins grande mobilité des agglomérats et particules
de sol les uns par rapport aux autres.

D. <u>Garezustand</u> (m)
Der chemische, physikalische und biologische Zustand
von bebautem Boden (<u>siehe</u> Gare).

Esp. <u>capacidad de laboreo</u>
Una condición física de suelos cultivados.

P. <u>sazão</u>
<u>ensejo cultural</u>
<u>condição estrutural do solo</u>
<u>estado físico</u>
Condição física dum solo em relação à sua aptidão para
o crescimento duma planta determinada.

I. <u>stato</u> (m) <u>di lavorazione</u> (f)
Una condizione fisica del terreno lavorato.

Nl. <u>kruimeling</u>
Mate waarin de bodem uit kruimels bestaat.

S. <u>(jordens) strukturtillstånd</u>
Fysikaliskt tillstånd hos en odlad jord.

Eng. ---------------
        Easily worked to a considerable depth.

F.   ---------------
        Facilement labourable à profondeurs considerables.

D.   tiefgründig
        Bis in grössere Tiefe leicht zu arbeiten.

Esp. ---------------
        Facilmente laborable a una profundidad considerable.

P.   ---------------
        Fàcilmente trabalhado até uma espessura considerável.

I.   ---------------
        Facilmente lavorabile a grande profondità.

Nl.   diep
        Gemakkelijk bewerkbaar tot op een aanzienlijke diopte.

S.   ---------------
        Med hårdare lager först på större djup.

Eng. <u>plow(plough)sole</u>
>   Layer of soil compacted by passage of the plow
>   (plough).

F. <u>fonds de raie au labour</u>
>   Couche de sol rendue compacte par le passage de
>   la charrue.

D. <u>Pflugsohle</u> (f)
>   Durch das Pflügen verdichtete Bodenschicht.

Esp. <u>piso de arado</u>
>   Capa de suelo compactada por el paso del arado.

P. <u>calo de lavoura</u>
>   Camada de solo tornado compacta pela passagem
>   da charrua.

I. <u>crosta</u> (m) <u>di lavorazione</u> (f)
>   Uno strato di terreno reso compatto da ripetuti
>   passaggi dell'aratro.

Nl. <u>ploegzool</u>
>   Een grondlaag, die in elkaar is gedrukt onder
>   invloed van het ploegen.

S. <u>plogsula</u>
>   Ett jordskikt som tillpackats av plogen vid
>   plöjningen.

Eng. <u>top soil</u>
        The layer of soil moved in cultivation;   the
        A horizon.

F.   <u>couche arable</u>
        La couche de sol remuée par la culture.

D.   <u>Ackerkrume</u> (f)
        Die bei der Bestellung bewegte Bodenschicht,
        häufig identisch mit dem A-Horizont.

Esp. <u>capa arable</u>
        La capa del suelo removida en el cultivo;
        el horizonte A.

P.   <u>solo superficial</u>
        A camada arável;   o horizonte A.

I.   <u>terreno (m) superficiale</u>
      <u>suolo (m) superficiale</u>
        Lo strato di terreno scommosso durante una
        lavorazione;   l'orizzonte A.

Nl.   <u>bouwvoor</u>
        De laag van de grond, die bij het bebouwen
        wordt omgewerkt.
      <u>bovengrond</u>
        De bovenste grondlaag, de A horizont.

S.   <u>matjord</u>
        Det översta omblandade skiktet av åkerjorden,
        karakteriserat genom likformig inblandning av
        organisk substans.

G10

Eng. <u>subsoil</u>
Part of a soil between the layer normally used in
tillage and the depth to which most plant roots grow.

F. <u>sous-sol</u>
Partie du sol située au-dessous de la couche
habituellement travaillée par les instruments de
culture.

D. <u>Untergrund</u> (m)
Unterer Teil eines Bodens, den durchwurzelten Raum
unterhalb der Ackerkrume umfassend.

Esp. <u>subsuelo</u>
Parte inferior del suelo.

P. <u>subsolo</u>
Camada inferior do solo.

I. <u>sottosuolo</u> (m)
Parte del suolo compresa tra il terreno normalmente
lavorato e la profondità a cui giungono gli apparati
radicali.

Nl. <u>ondergrond</u>
Deel van de grond onder de bouwvoor.

S. <u>alv</u>
Matjordens underlag.

Eng.   <u>manure</u>
      Animal droppings.

F.   <u>fumier</u>
      Mélange de litière et de déjections animales.

D.   <u>Stallmist</u> (m)
      Organischer Wirtschaftsdünger der durch Verrot-
      tung tierischer Exkremente und Einstreu gewonnen
      wird.

Esp.   <u>estiércol</u>
      Excrementos de animales.

P.   <u>estrume</u>
      Escremento de animais.

I.   <u>letame</u> (m)
   <u>concio</u> (m)
      Deiezioni animali, stagionate e trasformate.

Nl.   <u>stalmest</u>
      Dierlijke uitwerpselen.

S.   <u>stallgödsel</u>
   <u>naturlig gödsel</u>
      Exkrementer från djur, samt inbl. strömedel.

Eng. <u>fertilizer requirement</u>
        Estimated need for fertilizer.

F.   <u>besoin en engrais</u>
        Quantité d'engrais évaluée pour répondre aux
        exigences d'une culture.

D.   <u>Düngebedarf</u> (m)
        Geschätzter Düngebedarf.

Esp. <u>requerimiento de abonos</u>
        Necesidad estimada de abonos.

P.   <u>necessidade em adubo</u>
        Quantidade determinada necessária de fertilizante.

I.   <u>esigenza</u> (f) <u>di principi</u> (m p) <u>nutritivi</u>
        Necessità stimata di fertilizzante.

Nl.   <u>(kunst)mest behoefte</u>
        Geschatte behoefte aan kunstmest.

S.   <u>gödslingsbehov</u>
        Uppskattat behov av gödselmedel.

Eng. <u>amendment</u>
Work or material making soil more productive.

F. <u>amendement</u>
Travail ou matière tendant à améliorer les pro-
priétés physiques du sol.

D. <u>Bodenverbesserungsmittel</u> (n)
Arbeit oder andere Hilfsmittel, die den Boden
ertragsfähiger machen.

Esp. <u>enmienda</u>
Labores o materiales que hacen al suelo más pro-
ductivo.

P. <u>correctivos</u>
Materiais que tendem a melhorar as propriedades
físico-químicas do solo e, por conseguinte, torná-
lo mais produtivo.

I. <u>ammendamento</u> (m)
Lavori o materiali che rendono più produttivo il
terreno; mezzi che migliorano.

Nl. <u>grond verbeteraar</u>
Stof, die een grond geschikter maakt voor planten-
groei.

S. <u>jordförbättringsmedel</u>
Åtgärd el. material som höjer jordens produktions-
förmåga.

G14

Eng. <u>lime requirement</u>
Amount of CaO needed to make soil nearly neutral (U.K.).
Amount of ground limestone or any other specified liming
material required to raise the pH of an acid soil to any
desired value for a particular crop under field conditions (U.S.).

F. <u>besoin en chaux</u>
Quantité de CaO nécessaire pour amener le sol au
voisinage de la neutralité.

D. <u>Kalkbedarf</u> (m)
Menge CaO, die benötigt wird, um einen Boden annähernd
neutral zu machen.

Esp. <u>necesidad de cal</u>
Cantidad de cal finamente molida que se necesita para
llevar el pH del suelo cerca del punto de neutralidad.

P. <u>necessidade de cal</u>
Quantidade de calcário moido necessária para aproximar
o pH do solo da neutralidade.

I. <u>bisogno</u> (m) <u>di calce</u> (f)
Quantità di CaO per rendere il terreno quasi neutro.

Nl. <u>kalkbehoefte</u>
Hoeveelheid fijn gemalen kalk ($CaCO_3$) nodig om een grond
ongeveer neutraal te maken.

S. <u>kalkbehov</u>
Den mängd kalk som erfordras för att jorden skall bli
nästan neutral.

Section H

SOIL FORMATION, MORPHOLOGY

FORMATION DES SOLS, MORPHOLOGIE

FORMACION DEL SUELO, MORFOLOGIA

Eng. <u>pedosphere</u>
    The part of the Earth in which soil-forming processes
    occur.

F. <u>pédosphère</u>
    Partie de l'écorce terrestre dans laquelle les proces-
    sus de formation du sol ont lieu.

D. <u>Pedosphäre</u> (f)
    Der Teil der Erdoberfläche in dem sich Boden bildet.

Esp. <u>pedósfera</u>
    La parte de la capa terrestre en la cual se desarrollan
    los procesos de formación del suelo.

P. <u>pedosfera</u>
    Parte da crosta terrestre onde têm lugar os processos
    de formação do solo.

I. <u>pedosfera</u> (f)
    La parte della Terra in cui avviene il processo della
    formazione del terreno.

Nl. <u>pedosfeer</u>
    Het deel van de aardkorst, waarin de bodemvorming plaats
    vindt.

S. <u>pedosfär</u>
    Det yttersta lagret av jordskorpan, i vilket jordmåns-
    processerna äro verksamma.

167

Eng. <u>pedogenesis</u>
    The formation of soil from parent material.

F. <u>pédogenèse</u>
    Synonyme de formation du sol.

D. <u>Bodenbildung</u> (f)
    Entstehung des Bodens aus dem Ausgangsgestein unter
    dem Einfluss der bodenbildenden Faktoren.

Esp. <u>pedogénesis</u>
    La formación del suelo a partir de la roca madre.

P. <u>génese do solo</u>
    <u>pedogénese</u>
    Formação de solo a partir do material originário.

I. <u>pedogenesi</u> (f)
    La formazione del terreno dalla roccia madre.

Nl. <u>bodemvorming</u>
    De vorming van een bodem uit moedermateriaal.

S. <u>jordmånsbildning</u>
    Modermaterialets ombildning till en jordmån.

Eng. parent rock
      The rock from which parent material is formed.

F. roche-mère
      La roche à partir de laquelle se forme le sol.

D. Muttergestein (n)
      Gestein, aus dem durch Verwitterung Boden entsteht.

Esp. roca madre
      La roca a partir de la cual se forma el suelo.

P. rocha mãe
      A rocha a partir da qual se forma o material
      originário.

I. roccia (f) madre
      La roccia da cui si è originato il substrato o il
      materiale del terreno.

Nl. moedergesteente
      Het gesteente waaruit het moedermateriaal is gevormd.

S. moderbergart
      Den bergart som utgör en jords ursprungsmaterial.

H4

Eng.   <u>parent material</u>
        Unconsolidated material from which a soil is presumed
        to be formed.

F.   <u>matériau originel</u>
        Matériau provenant de la décomposition de la roche-
        mère, à partir duquel se forme le sol.

D.   <u>Ausgangsmaterial</u> (n)
        Alle Stoffe, die zur Bildung des Bodens beitragen.

Esp.   <u>roca madre</u>
        El material no consolidado a partir del cual se forma
        el suelo.

P.   <u>material originário</u>
        O material não consolidado a partir do qual se forma
        o solo.

I.   <u>substrato</u> (m)
        Il materiale dal quale si forma il terreno.

Nl.   <u>moedermateriaal</u>
        Het materiaal waaruit de bodem is gevormd.

S.   <u>modermaterial</u>
        (Den lösa avlagring) det lösa material i vilket jord-
        månsbildning äger rum.

Eng. <u>rhizosphere</u>
 The immediate neighbourhood of plant roots.

F. <u>rhizosphère</u>
 Partie du sol en contact immédiat avec les racines.

D. <u>Rhizosphäre</u>
 Die unmittelbare Umgebung der Pflanzenwurzeln.

Esp. <u>rizosfera</u>
 Zona inmediata a las raíces de las plantas.

P. <u>rizosfera</u>
 Parte do solo em que se desenvolvem as raizes das
 plantas.

I. <u>rizzosfera</u> (f)
 Le immediate vicinanze delle radici delle piante.

Nl. <u>rhizospheer</u>
 Doorwortelde grondlaag.

S. <u>rhizosfär</u>
 Den del av jordskorpan, i vilken växternas rötter
 utbreda sig.

Eng. <u>morphology</u>
        Pattern of horizons and structural aggregates that
        makes up the soil.

F. <u>morphologie</u>
        Aspect du sol apprécié par la vue et le toucher.

D. <u>Morphologie</u> (f)
        Lehre von den äusserlich erkennbaren Merkmalen des
        Bodens.

Esp. <u>morfología</u>
        Rasgos que presentan los horizontes y agregados
        estructurales que constituyen el perfil del suelo.

P. <u>morfologia</u>
        Constituição física do solo, incluindo a textura,
        a estrutura, a porosidade, a consistência e a cor
        dos vários horizontes e a sua distribuição no per-
        fil do solo.

I. <u>aspetto</u> (m) <u>fisico del terreno</u>
        La costituzione fisica del terreno come osservato
        con l'occhio e col tatto.

Nl. <u>(bodem)morfologie</u>
        De leer en de beschrijving van de uiterlijk kenbare
        eigenschappen van de grond.

S. <u>markmorfologi</u>
        Läran om jordmånens yttre, synliga kännetecken.

Eng. <u>mature</u>
Having a full developed profile (U.K.).
Having clearly developed genetic horizons (U.S.).

F. <u>évolué</u>
Très nettement différencié de la roche-mère.

D. <u>reif</u>
Mit voll entwickeltem Profil.

Esp. <u>maduro</u>
Que tiene un perfil completamente desarrollado.

P. <u>maduro</u>
Com perfil bem desenvolvido e em equilíbrio com
o meio ambiente.

I. <u>maturo</u>
Che ha un profilo completamente sviluppato.

Nl. <u>rijp</u>
Met een volledig ontwikkeld profiel.

S. <u>mogen, (val utvecklad jordmån)</u>
Har en väl utvecklad profil.

H8

Eng. **immature**
      Lacking a well-developed profile.

F. **peu évolué**
      Peu différencié de la roche-mère.

D. **unreif**
      Ohne gut entwickeltes Profil.

Esp. **inmaturo**
      Que carece de un perfil bien desarrollado.

P. **imaturo**
      Que não possui perfil bem desenvolvido.

I. **immaturo**
      Che manca di un profilo ben sviluppato.

Nl. **niet rijp, onrijp**
      Zonder een goed ontwikkeld profiel.

S. **omogen**
   outvecklad
      Saknar en väl utbildad profil.

Eng.   leach
      Remove soluble material by passing a liquid through
      soil.

F.   lessiver
      Déplacer une matière par entraînement à l'eau.

D.   auswaschen
      Lösliches Material durch Wasser entfernen.

Esp.   lixiviar
      Remover material soluble por lavados.

P.   lavar
      Remover material solúvel por lavagem.

I.   lisciviare
      Asportare del materiale solubile per mezzo del
      dilavamento.

Nl.   uitspoelen
      Oplosbare stof door uitwassen verwijderen.

S.   urlaka
      Avlägsna lösligt material genom urtvättning.

H10

Eng. <u>degradation</u>
> Change in soil due to increased leaching.

F. <u>dégradation (du sol)</u>
> Evolution d'un sol dans un sens défavorable à
> son utilisation agricole.

D. <u>Degradierung</u> (f)
> Veränderung in einem Boden infolge verstärkter
> Auslaugung.

Esp. <u>degradación</u>
> Cambio en el suelo debido al aumento de la
> lixiviación.

P. <u>degradação</u>
> Mudança produzida por alteração das condições
> primativas.

I. <u>degradazione</u> (f)
> Cambiamento entro il terreno dovuto all'aumentata
> lisciviazione.

Nl. <u>degradatie</u>
> Verandering in een grond tengevolge van toenemende
> uitloging.

S. <u>försämring, (degradation)</u>
> Förändring av jordmånen förorsakad av ökad urlakning
> och sänkt pH-värde.

Eng. <u>truncated</u>
  Having lost all or part of the upper horizons.

F. <u>tronqué</u>
  Ayant perdu la totalité ou une partie d'un ou
  des horizons supérieurs.

D. <u>verstümmelt</u>
  Bezeichnet ein Profil dessen oberer Teil ganz
  oder teilweise abgetragen wurde.

Esp. <u>truncado</u>
  Que ha perdido todo o parte del horizonte
  superior.

P. <u>decapitado</u>
  Que perdeu no total, ou em parte, o horizonte
  superior.

I. <u>troncato</u>
  Che ha perso tutto o parte dell'orizzonte
  superiore.

Nl. <u>afgeknot</u>
  De gehele of gedeeltelijke bovenste horizont
  verloren hebbend.

S. <u>stympad</u>
  <u>dekapiterad</u>
  Hela eller delar av de övre markskikten ha ero-
  derats bort.

Eng.   <u>endodynamomorphic</u>
        Influenced mainly by parent material.

F.   <u>endodynamomorphe</u>
        Essentiellement influencé par la roche-mère.

D.   <u>endodynamomorph</u>
        Hauptsächlich durch das Ausgangsmaterial beeinflusst.

Esp.   <u>endodinamomórfico</u>
        Influido principalmente por la roca madre.

P.   <u>endodinamomórfico</u>
        Influenciado principalmente pelo material originário.

I.   <u>endodinamorfo</u>
        Influenzato prevalentemente dalla roccia madre.

Nl.   <u>endodynamomorph</u>
        In hoofdzaak beïnvloed door het moedermateriaal.

S.   <u>endodynamomorf</u>
        Huvudsakligen betingad av ursprungsmaterialet.

Eng.   ectodynamomorphic
   Shaped by influences other than parent material.

F.   ectodynamomorphe
   Ayant subi d'autres influences que celle de la
   roche-mère.

D.   ektodynamomorph
   Vornehmlich durch äussere Einflüsse gestaltet und
   nich durch das Muttergestein (vgl. endodynamomorph).

Esp.   ectodinamomórfico
   Formado por otras influencias distintas a las de
   la roca madre.

P.   ectodinamomórfico
   Formado por outras influências que não sejam as do
   material originário.

I.   ectodinamorfo
   Trasformazione dovuta a influenze esterne e non
   dalla roccia madre.

Nl.   ectodynamomorph
   Gevormd door andere invloeden dan die van het moeder-
   materiaal.

S.   ektodynamomorf
   Bildad huvudsakligen under inflytande av andra fak-
   torer än ursprungsmaterialet.

H14

Eng. <u>hydromorphic</u>
Developed in presence of excess water all or part
of the time.

F. <u>hydromorphe</u>
Formé en présence d'eau.

D. <u>hydromorph</u>
Durch Wasser gestaltet.

Esp. <u>hidromórfico</u>
Desarrollado en presencia de agua en exceso temporal
o permanentemente.

P. <u>hidromórfico</u>
Que se forma na presença da água.

I. <u>idromorfo</u>
Che si é sviluppato in presenza di acqua.

Nl. <u>hydromorph</u>
Gevormd bij aanwezigheid van water.

S. <u>hydromorf</u>
Utvecklad i närvaro av vatten.

Section I

PROFILE CHARACTERS, HORIZONS

PROFILS, HORIZONS

CARACTERES DEL PERFIL, HORIZONTES

Eng.   profile
         Vertical section of soil showing sequence of horizons
         from surface to parent material.

F.   profil
         Succession des horizons de la surface à la roche-mère.

D.   Bodenprofil (n)
         (An einem senkrechten Einschnitt sichtbar gemachter)
         Aufbau des Bodens von der Oberfläche bis zum Ausgangs-
         material.

Esp.   perfil de suelo
         Sucessión de horizontes desde la superficie hasta la
         roca madre.

P.   perfil
         Sequência de horizontes desde a superfície até ao
         material originário.

I.   profilo (m)
         Sezione verticale del terreno che mostra la serie
         degli orizzonti dalla superficie fino alla roccia
         madre.

Nl.   profiel
         Opeenvolging van horizonten van het oppervlak tot op
         het moedermateriaal.

S.   profil
         En följd av markhorisonter från ytan ned till ursprungs-
         materialet.

Eng.   monolith
            Vertical section taken from soil.

F.   monolithe de sol
            Prisme vertical de sol prélevé en un bloc.

D.   Bodenmonolith (m)
        Bodenprofil (n)
            Aus einem Boden entnommener vertikaler Ausschnitt.

Esp.   monolito de suelo
            Sección vertical extraida del suelo.

P.   monolito do solo
            Secção vertical retirada do solo.

I.   campione (m) completo di un profilo (m)
            Sezione vertical estratta da un terreno.

Nl.   bodemmonoliet
        lakfilm
            Een langs verticale doorsnede uitgestoken bodem-
            profiel.

S.   monolit
            Jordprofilprov i oförändrad lagring (vertikal
            sektion).

Eng. <u>horizon</u>
      Soil layer with features produced by soil-forming
      processes.

F. <u>horizon</u>
      Couche de sol ayant acquis des caractères distinctifs.

D. <u>Horizont</u> (m)
      Eine kennzeichnende Schicht eines Bodentyps.

Esp. <u>horizonte</u>
      Una capa que ha adquirido rasgos distintivos.

P. <u>horizonte</u>
      Uma camada que adquiriu características bem definidas
      produzidas pelos processos de formação do solo.

I. <u>orizzonte</u> (m)
      Uno strato che ha acquisito caratteristiche particolari.

Nl. <u>horizont</u>
      Een laag, die onder invloed van bodemvorming bepaalde
      kenmerkende eigenschappen heeft verkregen.

S. <u>horisont</u>
      Ett avgränsat skikt med bestämda kännetecken.

14

Eng. **A horizon**
        The uppermost, eluvial layers of a soil profile.

F. **horizon-A**
        Horizon organique ou éluvial d'un profil de sol.

D. **A-Horizont**
        Der (im humiden Gebiet zuoberst liegende) Auswaschungs-
(oder Eluvial-) horizont eines Bodenprofils.

Esp. **horizonte A**
        Capa más superficial del perfil de un suelo general-
mente rica en materia orgánica y de la que los consti-
tuyentes minerales se pierden por lixiviación.

P. **horizonte A**
        Camada ou camadas superficiais dum perfil do solo
correspondentes à zona de eluviação.

I. **orizzonte A**
        Lo strato più superficiale eluviato di un profilo del
suolo.

Nl. **A-horizont**
        De bovenste, eluvial horizont van een bodemprofiel.

S. **A-horisont**
        Det övre, urlakade (eluviala) skiktet i en markprofil.

Eng. B horizon
           The illuvial layers of a soil profile.

F.   horizon B
           Couche illuviale d'un profil de sol.

D.   B-Horizont
           Der (im humiden Gebiet unter dem A-Horizont liegende)
           Einwaschungs- (oder Illuvial-) horizont eines Boden-
           profils.

Esp. horizonte B
           Parte iluviada del suelo que se encuentra inmediata-
           mente debajo del horizonte A.

P.   horizonte B
           Camada ou camadas dum perfil do solo correspondentes
           à zona de iluviação.

I.   orizzonte B
           Gli strati illuviati di un profilo di terreno.

Nl.   B-horizont
           De inspoelingslagen van een bodemprofiel.

S.   B-horisont
           Det anrikade illuviala lagret i en markprofil.

16

Eng. <u>C horizon</u>
Horizon of weathered rock material little affected by biological soil-forming processes.

F. <u>horizon C</u>
Roche-mère plus ou moins altérée d'un sol.

D. <u>C-Horizont</u>
Verwitterte Gesteinschicht durch biologische Boden-bildungsvorgänge unbeeinflusst.

Esp. <u>horizonte C</u>
Parte debilmente meteorizada del suelo, sobre la cual descanza el horizonte B.

P. <u>horizonte C</u>
Horizonte de rocha meteorizada, pràticamente não afectado pelos processos biológicos de formação do solo, e que é o material originário do solo.

I. <u>orizzonte C</u>
Orizzonte di roccia in via di alterazione, non intac-cato dai processi biológici che formano il terreno.

Nl. <u>C-horizont</u>
Horizont van verweerd gesteente, niet beinvloed door biologische bodemvormingsprocessen.

S. <u>C-horisont</u>
Det av jordmånsprocesserna föga berörda lagret under själva jordmånen.

Eng. D horizon
   Unweathered rock below the C horizon.

F.   horizon D
   Roche-mère non altérée (souvent confondu en français
   avec l'horizon C).

D.   D-Horizont
   Unverwittertes Gestein unterhalb des C-Horizontes (in
   Deutschland bisher mit C-Horizont zusammengefasst).

Esp. horizonte D
   Roca no meteorizada que se encuentra debajo del horizonte C.

P.   horizonte D
   Rocha meteorizada subjacente ao horizonte C.

I.   orizzonte D
   Roccia madre inalterata sotto l'orizzonte C.

Nl. D-laag
   Onverweerd gesteente onder de C-horizont.

S.   D-horisont
   Oförvittrad berggrund under lösa avlagringar.

Eng. F layer
      F horizon
          Layer of forest soil consisting of partly decomposed
          plant residues.

F.   horizon F
          Partie supérieure de la couche d'humus brut renfermant
          une quantité élevée de débris végétaux en voie de décom-
          position. (Non utilisé en français.)

D.   "F-Schicht"
      "F-Horizont"
          Übergangsschicht zwischen unzersetzten Waldstreu und
          H-Schicht in Auflagehumus. (Schwedischer Begriff.)

Esp. capa F
          La parte superior de una capa de humus fresco con
          residuos vegetales parcialmente descompuestos, pero en
          proceso activo de descomposición.

P.   camada F
      horizonte F
          Camada de fermentação existente no contacto do hori-
          zonte A_{oo} e A_o.

I.   strato F
      orizzonte F
          Strato del terreno forestale consistente parzialmente
          in residui decomposti di piante.

Nl.   F-horizont
          Bodemlaag bestaande uit gedeeltelijk verteerd strooisel.

S.   F-skikt
      F-horisont
          Den övre del av ett mor- (eller råhumus-) skikt, med
          relativt tydliga växtlämningar, där förmultningen är
          livlig.

Eng.   G horizon
        The horizon in which gley occurs.

F.   horizon G
        Horizon de gley.

D.   G-Horizont
        Für Gleiboden typischer Horizont mit Eisenoxydhydrat-
        Ausscheidungen.

Esp.   horizonte G
        Horizonte en el que aparece un material gris azuloso
        o gris óliva, más o menos pegajoso, compacto y a menudo
        sin estructura (horizonte gley).

P.   horizonte G
        O horizonte em que aparece glei.

I.   orizzonte G
        L'orizzonte in cui avviene il fenomeno "gley".

Nl.   G-horizont
        De horizönt, waarin gleyverschijnselen voorkomen.

S.   G-horisont
        (Glei-horisont) ett grått skikt med rostfärgade
        strimlor och fläckar, utbildad inom området mellan
        grundvattnets högsta och lägsta nivå.

Eng.   H layer
        H horizon
            Organic layer of forest soils with dark-coloured,
            structureless humus.

F.   horizon H
            Partie inférieure de la couche d'humus brut riche en
            materière organique colloïdale. (Non utilisé en
            français.)

D.   "H-Schicht"
        "H-Horizont"
            Unterste Schicht des Auflagehumus mit dunklem struktur-
            losem Humus. (Schwedischer Begriff.)

Esp.   horizonte H
            Parte inferior de una capa de humus fresco de color
            oscuro, no estructurado.

P.   camada H
        horizonte H
            A parte inferior duma camada de humus crú de côr escura
            e sem estrutura.

I.   strato H
        orizzonte H
            Corrisponde all'orizzonte A (H da humus).

Nl.   H-horizont
            Bodemlaag, voor het grootste deel bestaande uit goed
            veraarde amorphe organische stof.

S.   H-skikt
        H-horisont
            Det undre på humusämnen rika lagret i ett mor-
            (råhumus-) skikt.

Eng. **eluvial horizon**
    Layer from which material has been removed in solution
    or in water suspension and in which silt- and sand-
    sized particles have become concentrated.

F. **horizon éluvial**
    Couche (de sol) qui a été lessivée.

D. **Eluvialhorizont (m)**
    Schicht, die ausgelaugt wurde.

Esp. **horizonte eluvial**
    Capa de suelo que ha sido lixiviada.

P. **horizonte de eluviação**
    Camada que foi submetida a lavagem.

I. **orizzonte (m) eluviato**
    Strato del terreno che è stato lisciviato.

Nl. **uitgeloogde horizont**
    Laag, die uitgeloogd is.

S. **urlakningsskikt**
    Lager som urlakats i markprofil.

Eng. <u>illuvial horizon</u>.
Horizon that has received material in solution or
suspension from the upper part of the soil.

F. <u>horizon illuvial</u>
Couche de sol dans laquelle s'accumulent des éléments
provenant d'autres horizons du profil.

D. <u>Illuvialhorizont</u>
Schicht, in welcher sich ausgelaugte Stoffe anreichern,
die aus einer anderen Bodenschicht ausgewaschen wurden
(B-Horizont).

Esp. <u>horizonte iluvial</u>
Capa de suelo en la que se acumula algo.

P. <u>horizonte iluvial</u>
Camada de acumulação de materiais provenientes doutra
camada do solo.

I. <u>orizzonte</u> (m) <u>illuviale</u>
Strato in cui si accumula il materiale lisciviato da
un'altra parte del terreno.

Nl. <u>illuviale horizont</u>
<u>inspoelings horizont</u>
Laag waarin iets is opgehoopt.

S. <u>anrikningshorisont</u>
Skikt där anrikning sker.

Eng. permafrost
        Permanently frozen ground.

F.   tjäle
        Horizon gelé en permanence.

D.   Permafrost (m), (Tjäle)
        Dauernd gefrorener Horizont.

Esp. -----------------
        Horizonte permanentemente helado.

P.   -----------------
        Horizonte permanentemente gelado.

I.   tjale (m)
        Orizzonte perennemente gelato.

Nl.   permafrost
      tjäle
        Permanent bevroren horizont.

S.   ständig tjäle
        Ständigt fruset skikt.

Eng.   gley

Yellow and gray mottling in the soil produced by partial
oxidation and reduction of iron caused by intermittent
waterlogging.

F.   gley

Coloration gris verdâtre produite dans le sol par la
réduction partielle des composés ferriques sous
l'influence de conditions d'anaérobiose crées par la
présence intermittente de l'eau.

D.   Glei (m)

Unter dem Einfluss des Wechsels von extremer Durch-
feuchtung (Grundwasser und Staunässe) und Austrocknung
entstandene Flecken im Boden bedingt durch beweglich
gewordenes und wieder ausgefälltes Eisen.

Esp.   gley

Capa de color amarillo pálido o gris producida por
la oxidación y reducción parciales de los compuestos
férricos, a consecuencia de anegamientos intermitentes.

P.   "glei"

Mosqueado amarelo e cinzento do solo devido a oxidação
e redução parciais do ferro causado por encharcamento
intermitente.

I.   gley

Pomellatura gialla e grigia del terreno prodotta da
parziale ossidazione e riduzione del ferro causata da
impregnamento d'acqua intermittente.

Nl.   gley

Roestbruine en grijze vlekken, veroorzaakt door partiele
oxydatie en reductie van ijzer onder invloed van fluc-
tuaties in de grondwaterstand.

S.   glei

Rostfärgade utfällningar från grundvattnet.

Eng.   <u>bleached sand</u>
      Sand which has become pale owing to leaching.

F.   <u>sable lessivé</u>
      Sable devenu plus clair par suite de lessivage.

D.   <u>Bleichsand</u> (m)
      Sand, der infolge Auslaugung usw. bleich geworden ist.

Esp.   <u>arena descolorida</u>
      Arena que ha palidecido debido a la lixiviación, etc.

P.   <u>areia lavada</u>
      Areia que devido à lavagem se tornou mais esbranquiçada.

I.   <u>sabbia</u> (f) <u>sbiancata</u>
      Sabbia che si è schiarita per lisciviazione.

Nl.   <u>gebleekt zand</u>
   <u>bleekzand</u>
      Zand dat bleek is geworden tengevolge van uitspoeling.

S.   <u>bleksand</u>
      Sand som har blekts på grund av urlakning.

Eng. <u>crotovine, (krotovina)</u>
Filled-in animal burrow in soil.

F. <u>crotovina</u>
Terrier de rongeurs, rempli de débris terreux et
organiques et de calcaire.

D. <u>Krotovine</u>
Mit erdigem, kalkigem und organischem Material
ausgefüllter Tierbau. (Russische Bezeichnung.)

Esp. <u>crotovina</u>
Madriguera rellena de restos terrosos y orgánicos.

P. <u>crotovina</u>
Cavidade feita por animais e preenchida com material
do solo.

I. <u>crotovina</u>
Cavità riempita.

Nl. <u>crotovina</u>
Opgevulde dierengang.

S. <u>krotovina</u>
Gångar grävda av större djur i jorden, sedan fyllda
med jordmaterial.

Eng. clay pan
           Dense subsoil horizon formed by washing down of clay
           or by synthesis of clay.

F.   horizon argileux compact
           Horizon argileux du sous-sol, résultant du lessivage
           ou de la néoformation sur place des éléments argileux.

D.   verdichtete Tonschicht (f)
           Dichter Untergrundhorizont, der durch Toneinwaschung
           oder durch Tonbildung entstanden ist.

Esp.   capa de arcilla
           Horizonté denso de subsuelo formado por arrastre de
           arcilla o por síntesis de arcilla.

P.   calo de argila
           Horizonte compacto de subsolo formado por iluviação ou
           por síntese do argila.

I.   banco (m) compatto argilloso
           Orizzonte compatto del sottosuolo formatosi da apporto
           di argilla o dalla sinteti di argilla.

Nl.   kleibank
           Verdichte horizont in de ondergrond, gevormd door naar
           beneden gespoelde klei of door nieuwvorming van klei.

S.   alvförtätning
           Förhårdnad i alven orsakad av nedslammat ler eller dyl.
           eventuellt av mekaniskt tryck.

Eng. <u>hard pan</u>
          Indurated or cemented layer of soil.

F. <u>horizon durci</u>
          Couche de sol fortement cohérente.

D. <u>Verdichtungshorizont</u> (m)
          Verhärtete oder zementierte Bodenschicht.

Esp. <u>capa dura</u>
          Horizonte endurecido o cementado.

P. <u>turo</u>
    <u>surraipa</u>
          Horizonte endurecido ou cimentado.

I. <u>neolite</u> (m)
          Orizzonte indurito o cementato.

Nl. <u>bank</u>
          Een verharde of verkitte horizont.

S. <u>skenhälla</u>
          Ett hårdnat eller sammankittat skikt i en markprofil.

Eng. iron pan
         Layer, usually of sand, cemented with iron oxides.

F.   alios ferrugineux
         Couche de sol cimentée par des oxydes de fer.

D.   ------------------
         Durch Eisenoxydhydrat verhärtete Bodenschicht.

Esp. capa ferruginosa
         Capa generalmente de arena, cementada por hierro.

P.   surraipa ferruginosa
         Camada, vulgarmente de areia, cimentada por óxidos de
         ferro.

I.   neolite (m) ferruginoso
      alios (m) ferruginoso
      ortstein (m) ferruginoso
      banco (m) inferiore ferruginoso
         Strato, generalmente sabbioso, cementato con ferro.

Nl.   oerbank
         Grondlaag, gewoonlijk bestaande uit zand aaneengekit
         door ijzer-verbindingen.

S.   järnskenhälla
         Skenhälla upkommen genom järnutfällningar.

Eng.   <u>ortstein</u>
        Hard, cemented B-horizon of a podzol.

F.   ----------

D.   <u>Ortstein</u> (m)
        Stark verhärteter B-Horizont des Podsolprofils.

Esp.   <u>alios</u>
        Capa de suelo duro y compacto que se forma durante
        el proceso de podsolización.

P.   <u>ortstein</u>
        Surraipa dura do horizonte B de um Podzol.

I.   <u>ortstein</u>
        Orizzonte B duro cementato di un podsolo.

Nl.   <u>oerbank</u>
       <u>humusoerbank</u>
       <u>koffieoerbank</u>
        Harde, bankvormige B-horizont van het podzolprofiel.

S.   <u>ortsten</u>
        Synonym för skenhälla, hård, sammankittad B-horisont
        i en podsolprofil.

Eng.   <u>orterde</u>
       Compacted B horizon of a podzol.

F.   ----------

D.   <u>Orterde</u> (f)
       Mässig verhärteter B-Horizont des Podsolprofils.

Esp.   <u>orterde</u>
       Horizonte B compacto de un podsol.

P.   <u>orterde</u>
       Surraipa branda do horizonte B de um Podzol.

I.   <u>orterde</u>
       Orizzonte B compatto di un podsolo.

Nl.   <u>losse oergrond</u>
       <u>los humusoer</u>
       <u>losse koffieoer</u>
       Verdichte, doch niet bankvormige B-horizont van het
       podzolprofiel.

S.   -------------
       Måttligt förhårdnad B-horisont i en podsolprofil.

Eng. <u>lime pan</u>
        Thick layer of calcium carbonate.

F.   <u>horizon d'accumulation calcaire</u>
        Dépôt épais de carbonate de calcium.

D.   ------------
        Dicker Kalk-Horizont.

Esp. <u>capa caliza</u>
        Depósito grueso de carbonato de calcio.

P.   <u>tufo calcário</u>
      <u>surraipa calcária</u>
        Depósito espesso e endurecido de carbonato de cálcio.

I.   <u>orizzonte (m) calcareo</u>
        Spesso deposito di carbonato di calcio.

Nl.   <u>kalkbank</u>
        Dikke afzetting van calcium-carbonaat in het profiel.

S.   <u>kalkavsättning</u>
        Skikt, huvudsakligen bestående av kalciumkarbonat.

Eng.   "nazzaz"
     A compact, impermeable pan, concretionary in character,
     occurring at a slight depth below the surface of red
     sandy soils in the Levant.

F.   "nazzaz"
     Couche compact imperméable, d'aspect concrétionné se
     formant à faible profondeur dans les sols rouges
     sableux du Levant.

D.   "Nazzaz"
     Eine feste, undurchlässige Konkretionsschicht, die in
     geringer Tiefe bei roten sandigen Böden in der Levante
     auftritt.

Esp.   "nazzaz"
     Capa compacta, impermeable que aparece casi debajo de
     la superficie de suelos rojos arenosos del Levante.

P.   "nazzaz"
     Uma camada compacta impermeável e de carácter concre-
     cionário que aparece a pequena profundidade nos solos
     vermelhos arenosos do Levante.

I.   "nazzaz"
     Uno strato compatto, impermeabile, di carattere concre-
     zionario, che si trova a piccola profondità sotto la
     superficie dei terreni sabbiosi rossi in Levante.

Nl.   "nazzaz"
     Compacte ondoorlatende bank, bestaande uit concreties
     di op geringe diepte voorkomt in rode zandgronden in
     de Levant.

S.   "nazzaz"
     Speciell tät och ogenomsläpplig skenhälla, som uppträder
     strax under markytan i röda sandiga jordar i Orienten.

Eng. concretion
     Aggregate formed round a nucleus by successive pre-
     cipitation of material.

F.   concrétion
     Elément durci formé par accumulation d'une matière qui
     se differencie du milieu.

D.   Konkretion (f)
     Aggregat das durch aufeinanderfolgende Ausfällung eines
     Stoffes um einen Kern gebildet wird.

Esp. concreción
     Agregado que se forma a consecuencia de la precipitación
     sucesiva de algunos compuestos químicos alrededor de un
     núcleo.

P.   concreção
     Agregado formado à volta de um núcleo por sucessivas
     precipitações de matéria.

I.   concrezione (f)
     Aggregato formato da successive precipitazioni di
     materiale (intorno al nucleo centrale).

Nl.   concretie
     Aggregaat gevormd door opeenvolgende neerslagen van een
     of andere stof.

S.   konkretion
     Aggregat bildat genom successiv utfällning omkring en
     kärna.

Eng. <u>ironstone</u>
(1) Rock whose mineral grains are cemented by iron oxide.
(2) Thick sheet of iron concretion.

F. <u>cuirasse ferrugineuse</u>
Bank rocheux dans lequel les minéraux du sol sont cimentés par de l'oxyde de fer.

D. <u>Raseneisenerz</u> (n)
<u>Sumpferz</u> (n)
Dicke Schicht von Eisenkonkretionen.

Esp. <u>piedra ferruginosa</u>
Capa gruesa de concreciones de hierro.

P. <u>couraça ferruginosa</u>
Camada espessa de concreções de ferro.

I. <u>orizzonte</u> (m) <u>compatto ferruginoso</u>
Banco spesso di concrezioni ferruginose (in prevalenza ossido di ferro).

Nl. <u>ijzersteen</u>
Dikke laag van ijzerconcreties.

S. <u>skenhälla</u>
Tjockt skikt av järnkonkretioner.

Eng. bog-iron ore
          Deposit of hydrated iron oxides found in swamps an
          peat mosses.

F.   _____
          Concrétions ferrugineuses trouvées dans les marais.

D.   Raseneisenerz (n)
          In verlandeten Sümpfen gefundene Eisen-Konkretionen.

Esp. mineral ferruginoso limonitico
          Concreciones de hierro encontradas en pantanos.

P.   olho de perdiz
      chumbinho
          Concreções de ferro que aparecem nos pântanos.

I.   ferro (m) delle paludi (f p)
          Concrezioni ferruginose che si trovano nelle paludi.

Nl.   moeras ijzererts
          Ijzerconcreties, die in moerassen worden aangetroffen.

S.   myrmalm
          Järnutfällningar, ofta i form av konkretioner, i
          myrar eller sjöar.

Eng.　pea iron
　　　　Small round concretions containing much iron oxide.

F.　pisolithe ferrugineux
　　　　Petite concrétion arrondie riche en oxyde de fer.

D.　Bohneisenerz (n)
　　　　Kleine runde Konkretionen, welche viel Eisenoxydhydrat
　　　　enthalten.

Esp.　perdigones
　　　　Pequeñas concreciones redondeadas que contienen mucho
　　　　hierro.

P.　concreção ferruginosa
　　　olho de perdiz
　　　chumbinho
　　　　Pequenas concreções arredondadas ricas em ferro.

I.　pisolite (f) ferruginosa
　　　　Piccole concrezioni rotondeggianti che contengono molto
　　　　ossido di ferro.

Nl.　korrelvormige ijzerconcreties
　　　　Kleine ronde concreties, die v∋ I ijzer bevatten.

S.　ärtmalm
　　　　Små runda konkretioner med hög järnhalt.

Eng.   calcareous crust
          Indurated horizon cemented with calcium carbonate.

F.   croûte calcaire
          Horizon durci cimenté par du calcaire.

D.   ------------
          Durch $CaCO_3$ verhärtete Schicht.

Esp.   tosca
          Horizonte endurecido cementado con carbonato de
          calcio.

P.   tufo
    tufo calcário
          Camada endurecida cimentada por carbonato de cálcio.

I.   crostone (m) calcareo
          Orizzonte indurito, cementato con carbonato di calcio.

Nl.   kalkhoudende harde laag
          Door kalk aaneengekitte harde laag.

S.   tosca
          Kalkrik skenhälla.

Eng.   <u>puppet</u>
   Lime concretion shaped like a small doll, found in loess.

F.   <u>poupée</u>
   Concrétion calcaire ayant des formes allongées et arrondies de statuettes primitives.

D.   <u>Kindel</u> (n)
   Kalkkonkretion von der Gestalt einer kleinen Puppe, in Löss vorkommend.

Esp.   <u>muñequita</u>
   Concreción caliza en forma de pequeñas muñecas.

P.   <u>"boneca"</u>
   Concreção calcária lembrando pequenas bonecas.

I.   <u>bambola</u> (f)
   Concrezione calcaria che ricorda la forma di piccoli fantocci.

Nl.   <u>poppetje</u>
   Kalkconcretie, die wat vorm betreft lijkt op een kleine pop.

S.   <u>markleka</u>
   Kalkkonkretion formad likt en liten docka.

Eng.   pseudo-mycelium
      Threadlike mineral formation resembling fungus growth.

F.   pseudo-mycelium
      Formation filiforme minérale ressemblant à un mycelium.

D.   Pseudomyzel (n)
      Fadenähnliches Ausbildung von Mineralien, die Pilz-
      hyphen gleicht.

Esp.   pseudo micelio
      Formación filiforme que se asemaja al crecimiento de
      hongos.

P.   pseudo micélio
      Formação filamentosa que se assemelha ao micélio de
      um fungo.

I.   pseudomicelio (m)
      Formazione filamentosa che rassomiglia lo sviluppo del
      micelio di un fungo.

Nl.   pseudo mycelium
      Op draden lijkende vorming, die op schimmelgroei lijkt.

S.   pseudomycel
      Trådlika bildningar likande svampmycel.

Section J

GEOLOGY, TOPOGRAPHY, CLIMATE

GEOLOGIE, TOPOGRAPHIE, CLIMAT

GEOLOGIA, TOPOGRAFIA, CLIMA

Eng. <u>alluvial</u>
>Deposited from flowing or still water.

F. <u>alluvial</u>
>Déposé par une eau.

D. <u>fluviatil (alluvial)</u>
>Durch fliessendes Wasser abgelagert.

Esp. <u>aluvial</u>
>Depositado por agua de río.

P. <u>aluvial</u>
>O que a água do rio depositou.

I. <u>alluviale</u>
>Depositatosi dalle acque che scorrono.

Nl. <u>alluviaal</u>
>Door of in water afgezet.

S. <u>alluvial</u>
>Avlagringar avsatta under postglacial tid.

Eng. <u>marl</u>
> Earthy calcareous material (U.K.).
> Earthy deposit of $CaCO_3$ formed in freshwater
> lakes (U.S.).

F. <u>marne</u>
> Formation constituée par un mélange de calcaire
> et d'argile.

D. <u>Mergel</u> (m)
> Mischung aus Ton und feinkornigem Kalk.

Esp. <u>marga</u>
> Material arcillo calizo.

P. <u>marga</u>
> Formação terrosa constituida por carbonato de
> cálcio ou dolomite misturado com argila.

I. <u>marna</u> (f)
> Formazione argillosa calcarea.

Nl. <u>mergel</u>
> Aardachtig, calciumcarbonaat-houdend materiaal.

S. <u>märgel</u>
> En på kalciumkarbonat rik alvjord.

Eng. <u>breccia</u>
Coarse angular fragments of rock cemented together.

F. <u>brèche</u>
Fragments de roches, grossiers et anguleux, cimentés
ensemble.

D. <u>Brekzie</u> (f)
Verfestigte, grobe, kantige Gesteinstrümmer.

Esp. <u>brecha</u>
Fragmentos de roca angulares y gruesos cementados
entre si.

P. <u>brecha</u>
Rocha constituida por fragmentos grosseiros e angulares
cimentados (subdivisão do conglomerado).

I. <u>breccia</u> (f)
Frammenti grossolani angolosi di roccia cementati
insieme.

Nl. <u>breccie</u>
Samengekitte, hoekige gesteente fragmenten.

S. <u>breccia</u>
Grövre kantiga bergartsfragment sammankittade av en
mellansubstans till en ny bergart.

217

J4

Eng.   <u>chert</u>
       Fine-grained stone consisting of nearly pure silica.

F.   <u>chaille</u>
       Type de pierre formée de silice presque pure.

D.   <u>Hornstein</u>
       Aus fast reiner amorpher Kieselsäure bestehender Stein.

Esp.   <u>pedernal</u>
       Piedra constituída casi puramente de sílice.

P.   <u>pederneira</u>
   <u>sílex</u>
       Rocha composta quase exclusivamente de sílica (princi-
       palmente calcedónia).

I.   <u>selce</u>
       Minerale costruito quasi esclusivamente di silice.

Nl.   <u>kiezel(ge)steen(te)</u>
       Steen uit vrijwel zuiver kiezelzuur bestaande.

S.   <u>hälleflinta</u>
       Bergart bestående av nästan ren kiseldioxid.

Eng. <u>caliche</u>
(1) Nitrate-bearing gravel rock of sodium-nitrate deposits.
(2) Thick deposit of firm to hard calcium carbonate (U.S.).

F.

Gravier sur roche de nitrate de soude, à haute teneur en nitrate.

D. <u>Caliche</u>
Nitrathaltige Ablagerungen der Natriumsalpeterführenden Schichten.

Esp. <u>caliche</u>
Depósito rocoso que contiene nitrato de sodio.

P. "<u>caliche</u>"
Depósitos de arenito contendo nitrato de sodio.

I. <u>caliche</u> (m)
Depositi de ghiaia contenenti nitrato o roccia di nitrato di sodio.

Nl. <u>caliche</u>
Nitraattrijk los of vast gesteente in natrium-nitraat afzettingen.

S. <u>caliche</u>
Råsalpeterlagren med rikligt innehåll av natrium-nitrat.

Eng.   peat
        Slightly decomposed vegetable matter accumulated in
        water.

F.   tourbe
        Matière végétale peu décomposée, à structure spongieuse
        accumulée dans l'eau.

D.   Torf (m)
        Unvollständig zersetzte, in Mooren angehäufte Pflanzen-
        substanz.

Esp.   turba
        Materia vegetal escasamente descompuesta acumulada en
        el agua.

P.   turfa
        Matéria vegetal ligeiramente decomposta acumulada em
        condições de humidade excessiva.

I.   torba (f)
        Sostanze vegetali accumulatesi nell'aéqua e leggermente
        decomposte.

Nl.   veen
        turf

        Enigszins verweerd, opgehoopt in water plantaardig
        materiaal.

S.   torv
        Anhopning under fuktiga förhållanden av obetydligt el.
        måttligt sönderdelade växtrester.

Eng. <u>till</u>
<u>boulder clay</u>
    Unstratified, unsorted glacial deposit.

F.   <u>dépôt morainique</u>
    Dépôt glaciaire non stratifié et non homogène.

D.   <u>Geschiebemergel</u> (m)
   <u>Tillit</u> (m)
    Ungeschichtete, unaufbereitete Gletscherablagerung.

Esp. <u>barro</u>
    Depósito glacial no estratificado ni clasificado.

P.   <u>depósito glacial</u>
   <u>terreno errático</u>
    Depósito glacial não estratificado.

I.   <u>till</u> (m)
   <u>deposito</u> (m) <u>morenico</u>
    Deposito glaciale non stratificato e non classificato
    secondo le dimensioni degli elementi.

Nl.   <u>keileem</u>
    Ongelaagde, ongesorteerde, glaciale afzetting.

S.   <u>morän</u>
    Osorterad avlagring avsatt av inlandsisar el. glaciärer.

Eng.   <u>laterite</u>
Buchanan's name for a red subsoil which hardens perma-
nently on exposure or has already hardened under
natural conditions.

F.   <u>latérite</u>
Nom donné par Buchanan à un sous-sol rouge qui durcit
à l'air. Matériau provenant d'une décomposition très
poussée de roches silicatées alumineuses, caractérisé
par son appauvrissement en silice et son enrichisse-
ment en hydroxydes de fer et d'alumine.

D.   <u>Laterit</u> (m)
Ursprünglich von Buchanan geprägtes Wort für sesquioxyd-
reiches rotes Material, das an der Luft hart wird, aus
dem in Indien Ziegel (<u>later</u>) gemacht werden.

Esp.   <u>laterita</u>
Nombre dado por Buchanan a un subsuelo rojo que se
endurece al quedar expuesto al aire.

P.   <u>laterite</u>
Nome dado por Buchanan a uma argila usada no India para
construções e que endurece muito por dissecação ao ar.

I.   <u>laterite</u> (f)
Denominazione di Buchanan per un sottosuolo rosso che
si indurisce quando esposto all'aria.

Nl.   <u>lateriet</u>
Buchanan's naam voor een rode ondergrond, die aan de
lucht blootgesteld hard wordt.

S.   <u>laterit</u>
Benämning på en röd alvjord som hårdnar i luften
(Buchanan).

Eng.   debris
        Accumulation of broken rock, soil material, organic
        residues, etc.

F.   débris (rocheux)
        fragments
        Accumulation des roches brisées, de matière organique
        morte, etc.

D.   Schutt (m)
        Anhäufung von abgebröckeltem Fels, totem organischem
        Material usw.

Esp.   desecho
        Acumulación de trozos de rocas, materia orgánica
        muerta, etc.

P.   detritos
        Acumulação de fragmentos rochosos, de matéria orgânica,
        etc.

I.   detrito (m)
        Accumulo di frammenti rocciosi, resti organici ecc.

Nl.   puin
        Accumulatie van verkleind gesteente, dode organische
        stof, enz.

S.   detritus
        Anrikning av mekaniskt vittrade bergarter, död organisk
        materia etc.

Eng.   <u>detrital fan</u>
          Cone-shaped deposit where valley enters plain.

F.   <u>cône de déjection</u>
          Dépôt en forme de cône à l'endroit où la vallée entre
          dans la plaine.

D.   <u>Schuttfächer</u> (m)
          Kegelformige Ablagerung, wo das Tal in die Ebene
          ausmündet.

Esp.   <u>cono de dejección</u>
          Depósito de forma cónica donde el valle entra en la
          llanura.

P.   <u>cone de dejecção</u>
          Depósito de forma cónica à entrada dos vales.

I.   <u>cono</u> (m) <u>di deiezione</u> (f)
          Deposito a forma di cono allo sbocco di una valle in
          una zona pianeggiante.

Nl.   <u>puinkegel</u>
          Kegelvormige afzetting op de plaats waar een dal in
          de vlakte uitkomt.

S.   <u>raskon</u>
          Konformad avlagring i brant sluttning.

Eng. talus
      colluvium
          Detritus accumulated at foot of a steep slope.

F.   dépôt colluvial détritique
      colluvion
          Débris accumulés au pied d'une pente raide.

D.   Hangschutt (m), (Colluvium) (n)
          Am Fuss eines Steilhangs abgelagerter Schutt.

Esp. derrubio
      depósito coluvial
          Detritos acumulados al pié de una cuesta empinada.

P.   detritos coluviais
      talude de desabamento
          Detritos acumulados no sopé duma encosta íngreme,
          sobretudo por acção da gravidade.

I.   detrito (m) di falda (f)
      colluvium
          Detrito accumulatosi ai piedi di una pendice scoscesa.

Nl.   hellingpuin
      colluvium
          Puin opgehoopt aan de voet van een steile helling.

S.   talus
      kolluvial avlagring
          Avlagring vid foten av en brant sluttning.

Eng.   desert pavement
            Surface of stones and rocks remaining after finer
            material has been blown away.

F.   "pavés du désert"
            Surfaces planes rocheuses des régions désertiques
            ou subdésertiques.

D.   "Wüstenpflaster"
            Pflasterartige Anordnung von Steinen in der Wüste,
            die zurückbleiben wenn das feinere Material weg-
            geblasen wurde.   (Ausdruck in Deutschland ungebraüch-
            lich).

Esp.   pavimento desértico
            Superficie de piedras y rocas que subsiste en zonas
            desérticas después que el material más fino ha sido
            arrastrado por el viento.

P.   crosta desértica
            O que fica dum solo cascalhento ou pedregoso depois
            da remoção, por erosão eólica, dos elementos texturais
            finos.

I.   fondo (m) desertico
            Superficie di sassi e rocce che rimangono dopo che il
            materiale più fine è stato asportato dal vento.

Nl.   keienvloei
            Laag, bestaande uit stenen en/of grind, die is over-
            gebleven, nadat het fijnere materiaal is uitgeblazen.

S.   blockterräng
            Yta där allt finmaterial eroderats bort så att i
            huvudsak sten och block återstår.

Eng.   desert varnish
        Glossy coating of stones, etc. in deserts.

F.   vernis du désert
        Revêtement luisant des roches, etc. dans les déserts.

D.   Wüstenlack (m)
        Glänzender Überzug auf Steinen usw. in Wüsten.

Esp.   barniz del desierto
        Revestimiento lustroso que se observa en las super-
        ficies de las piedras de las zonas desérticas.

P.   verniz do deserto
        Revestimento lustroso das pedras, etc. nos desertos.

I.   vernice (f) del deserto (m)
        Sottile copertura, quale vernice brillante sulle rocce,
        ecc. nei deserti.

Nl.   woestijnvernis
        Glanzend oppervlak van stenen enz. in woestijnen.

S.   "ökenfernissa"
        Glänsande ytskikt på stenar och dylikt i ökentrakter.

Eng.   <u>peneplain</u>
        An old land surface which has become nearly level.

F.   <u>pénéplaine</u>
        Ancienne région montagneuse aplanie.

D.   <u>Fastebene</u> (f), (<u>Peneplain</u>)
        Alte Landoberfläche, die fast ebcn geworden ist.

Esp.   <u>penillanura</u>
        Una antigua superficie de tierra que se ha vuelto
        casi llana.

P.   <u>peneplanície</u>
        Formação antiga da terra que com o tempo se tornou
        quase plana.

I.   <u>peneplano</u> (m)
     <u>semipiano</u> (m)
        La superficie di territori di vecchia formazione
        che e diventata quasi livellata.

Nl.   <u>peneplain</u>
     <u>schiervlakte</u>
        Een oud landoppervlak, dat bijna vlak is geworden.

S.   <u>peneplan</u>
        En nära nog plan landyta, utjämnad av geologiska
        krafter.

Eng. drainage basin
      catchment basin
            District drained by a river and its tributaries.

F.   bassin versant
            Région drainée par une rivière.

D.   Einzugsgebiet (n)
            Das durch einen Fluss entwässerte Gebiet.

Esp. cuenca de drenaje
            Región drenada por un río.

P.   bacia de drenagem
            Área drenada por um rio.

I.   bacino (m) scolante
            Superficie entro la quale il drenaggio viene eseguito
            da un fiume.

Nl.   stroomgebied
      afwateringsgebied
            Het gebied, waarvan het water door een rivier wordt
            afgevoerd.

S.   avrinningsområde
            Område som avvattnas av ett vattendrag.

Eng.　<u>watershed</u>
　　　　(1) The topographic boundary separating the waters
　　　　flowing into different rivers or drainage basins.
　　　　(2) An elevated tract of ground between two drainage
　　　　areas.
　　　　(3) A drainage basin (U.S.).

F.　　<u>ligne de partage des eaux</u>
　　　　Limite topographique séparant deux surfaces drainées
　　　　par des rivières différentes.
　　　<u>bassin</u>
　　　　Surface collectant l'eau vers une rivière.

D.　　<u>Wasserscheide</u> (f)
　　　　Die topographische Grenze, die die Einzugsgebiete zweier
　　　　Flüsse trennt.

Esp.　<u>hoya</u>
　　　　Límite topográfico que separa las aguas que desembocan
　　　　en diferentes ríos o cuencas de drenaje.

P.　　<u>bacia hidrográfica</u>
　　　　Bacia de drenagem;　zona drenada por um curso de água e
　　　　seus afluentes.

I.　　<u>spartiacque</u> (m)
　　　　(1) La cresta che divide due bacini imbriferi.
　　　　(2) Un tratto che divide due unità bacinali.

Nl.　<u>waterscheiding</u>
　　　　(1) De topografische grens tussen twee stromen, die tot
　　　　verschillende riviersystemen behoren.
　　　　(2) Strook grond tussen twee stroomgebienden.

S.　　<u>vattendelare</u>
　　　　Gränsen mellan vattendrags avvattningsområde.

Eng.   **first bottom**
      The normal flood plain of a stream.

F.   **plaine alluviale**
      Plaine d'inondation habituelle d'un fleuve.

D.   **Flussbett** (n)
      Die normale Laufrinne eines Flusses.

Esp.   **zona de inundación**
      Ribera inundable de un río.

P.   **primeiro terraço**
      A planura normalmente inundada pelas cheias.

I.   **letto** (m) **di piena** (f)
      Il piano che viene invaso dalle piene normali di un
      corso d'acqua.

Nl.   **riviervlakte**
      De vlakte waarin een rivier stroomt.

S.   **flodbädd**
      Bottnen i ett vattendrag.

Eng.   <u>second bottom</u>
>The first terrace above the normal flood plain of a stream.

F.   <u>terrasse inférieure</u>
<u>basse terrasse</u>
>Première terrasse au-dessus de la plaine d'inondation normale d'un fleuve.

D.   <u>Hochwasserbett</u> (n)
>Die erste Terrasse über der normalen Laufrinne eines Flusses.

Esp.   <u>ribera alta</u>
>La primera terraza sobre la ribera inundable de un río.

P.   <u>segundo terraço</u>
>O terraço imediatamente acima da várzea inundável.

I.   <u>terrazza</u> (f) <u>d'alveo</u> (m)
>La prima terrazza al di sopra del piano delle piene normali di un corso d'acqua.

Nl.   <u>laagterras</u>
>Het eerste terras boven de vlakte waarin een rivier stroomt.

S.   <u>strandterrass</u>
>Terrass eller andra strandmärken ovanför en älv eller annan vattenyta.

Eng.   climatic index
        Number condensing climatic data.

F.   indice climatique
        Nombre condensant des données climatiques.

D.   Klimaindex (m)
        Klimatische Daten ausdrückende Ziffer.

Esp.   índice climático
        Cifra que condensa datos climáticos.

P.   índice climático
        Número que sintetiza dados climáticos.

I.   indice (m) climatico
        Rapporto che sintetizza i dati climatici.

Nl.   klimaatfactor
        Cijfer, dat klimatologische gegevens tot uitdrukking
        brengt.

S.   klimatfaktor
        Medeltal som sammanfattar data beträffande klimatet.

Eng. effective precipitation
      That part of total precipitation which is of use to
      plants.

F.   pluie efficace
      Partie de précipitations totales utilisable par les
      plantes.

D.   nutzbare Regenmenge (f)
      Der Teil der gesamten Niederschläge, der von den Pflan-
      zen genutzt werden kann.

Esp. lluvia efectiva
      Aquella parte del total de la lluvia que puede ser
      utilizada por las plantas.

P.   precipitação util
      A parte da precipitação total que é posta á disposição
      das plantas.

I.   precipitazione (f) efficace
      Quella frazione della precipitazione totale che è utiliz-
      zata dalle piante.

Nl.   nuttige neerslag
      Dat deel van de totale neerslag dat beschikbaar is voor
      de planten.

S.   effektiv nederbörd
      Den del av den totala nederbörden som kommer växterna
      till godo.

Section K

MINERALOGY, CLAY MINERALS

MINERALOGIE, MINERAUX ARGILEUX

MINEROLOGIA, MINERALES ARCILLOSOS

Eng. <u>clay mineral</u>
(1) Any crystalline substance occurring in the clay fraction.
(2) A crystalline hydrous layer silicate.

F. <u>minéral des argiles</u>
Substances minérales constituant la fraction argile.

D. <u>Tonmineral</u> (m)
In Ton vorkommendes, kristalline Substanz (meist nur für Verwitterungsneubildungen gebraucht).

Esp. <u>minerales de arcilla</u>
Silicatos cristalinos hydratados que se encuentran en la arcilla.

P. <u>minerais das argilas</u>
Silicatos hidratados cristalinos que constituem as argilas.

I. <u>minerale</u> (m) <u>delle argille</u>
Un silicato idrato, cristallino, che si riscontra nell'argilla.

Nl. <u>kleimineraal</u>
Kristallijn (hydro)silicaat, voorkomend in de klei-fractie van grond.

S. <u>lermineral</u>
Kristallina, vattenhaltiga silikat och hydroxider som ha sin huvudutbredning i leror och andra finkorniga jordarter.

Eng.   primary mineral
      Homogeneous constituent of unweathered rock (U.K.).
      Single crystal species of unweathered rock or soil
      (U.S.).

F.   minéral primitif
      Minéral inaltéré dé la roche mère.

D.   primäres Mineral (n)
      Mineral das aus dem Schmelzfluss stammt.

Esp.   mineral primario
      Constituyente homogéneo de una roca no meteorizada.

P.   mineral primário
      Componente homogénio de rocha não meteorizada ou do
      solo.

I.   minerale (m) primario
      Costituente omogeneo della roccia inalterata.

Nl.   primair mineraal
      Homogeen kristallijn bestanddeel van onverweerd
      gesteente.

S.   primärt mineral
      Enhetlig beståndsdel i den oförvittrade berggrunden.

Eng. secondary mineral
>   Recognizable substance formed from the weathering pro-
>   ducts of primary minerals.

F. minéral secondaire
>   Substance formée à partir des produits de décomposition
>   de la roche.

D. sekundäres Mineral (n)
>   Verwitterungsneubildung aus primären Mineralen.

Esp. mineral secundario
>   Substancia formada a partir de los productos de descom-
>   posición de una roca.

P. mineral secundário
>   Substância formada a partir dos minerais primários
>   durante os processos de meteorização das rochas e de
>   formação do solo.

T. minerale (m) secondario
>   Minerale formatosi dai prodotti della alterazione di
>   una roccia durante la formazione del terreno.

Nl. secundair mineraal
>   Substantie gevormd bij nieuwvorming van gesteente.

S. sekundärt mineral
>   Mineral bildat under jordmånsbildningen antingen
>   direkt genom omvandling av primära mineral eller
>   genom nybildning ur nedbrytningsprodukter av primära
>   mineral.

Eng. <u>montmorillonite series</u>
Isomorphous series of 2:1 layer silicates with great
expansion along the c-axis; two silicon-oxygen sheets
are condensed with one hydroxide sheet (Al, Mg, Fe isomorphous).

F. <u>groupe de la montmorillonite</u>
Minéraux argileux dans lesquels deux feuillets de
silicium oxygénés sont condensés avec un feuillet
d'hydroxyde (Al, Mg ou Fe).

D. <u>Montmorillonit-Gruppe</u> (f)
Tonminerale, bei denen zwei Silizium-Oxyd-Schichten mit
einer Hydroxyd-Schicht (Al, Mg, oder Fe) verbunden sind.

Esp. <u>grupo de la montmorillonita</u>
Minerales de arcilla y oxígeno en los cuales a cada
2 capas de sílice y oxígeno corresponde una de hydróxido
(Al, Mg o Fe).

P. <u>grupo da montmorilonite</u>
Minerais das argilas em que a cada duas folhas de
silíco-oxigénio corresponde uma de hidroxido de Al, Mg
ou Fe.

I. <u>gruppo</u> (m) <u>della montmorillonite</u> (f)
Minerali delle argille in cui due strati di silice e
ossigeno sono collegati con uno strato di idrossidi
(Al, Mg o Fe).

Nl. <u>montmorillonietgroep</u>
Kleimineralen waarin twee SiO_2 lagen verbonden zijn
door een hydroxyde laag (Al, Mg of Fe).

S. <u>montmorillonitgruppen</u>
Svällbara lermineral med gitter, uppbyggda av två
kiselsyreskikt, förenade med ett hydroxidskikt med
Al, Mg eller Fe.

Eng. <u>illite series</u>
<u>hydrous micas</u>
2:1 layer silicate clay, mica-like, of lower potassium
content than micas.

F. <u>groupe de l'illite</u>
<u>groupe des hydromicas</u>
Minéraux argileux riches en potassium.

D. <u>Illit-Gruppe</u> (f)
<u>Illite</u> (m p)
<u>glimmerähnliche Tonmineralen</u> (n p)
Glimmerähnliche Tonminerale mit weniger Kalium und mehr
Wasser als die eigentlichen Glimmer.

Esp. <u>grupo de la ilita</u>
<u>grupo de las micas hidratadas</u>
Minerales de arcilla con un alto contenido de potasio.

P. <u>grupo da ilite</u>
<u>grupo das micas hidratadas</u>
Minerais das argilas contendo potássio na sua estrutura
cristalina.

I. <u>gruppo</u> (m) <u>dell'illite</u> (f)
<u>gruppo</u> (m) <u>della mica</u> (f)
Minerali dell'argilla simili alla mica con un forte contenuto in potassio.

Nl. <u>illietgroep</u>
<u>gehydrateerde micagroep</u>
Kleimineraal met een hoog kaligehalte.

S. <u>illitgruppen</u>
<u>hydraterad glimmergrupp</u>
Glimmerartade, ej svällbara lermineral, uppbyggda av
två kiselsyreskikt, förenade med ett hydroxidskikt;
från de verkliga glimrarna skilja de sig genom högre
vatten- och lägre kaliumhalt.

241

K6

Eng.   kaolin family
        Family of 1:1 layer silicates in which each silicon-
        oxygen sheet is condensed with one aluminium-hydroxide
        sheet.

F.   groupe du kaolin
        Minéraux argileux dans lesquels chaque feuillet
        silicium-oxygène est condensé avec un feuillet
        d'hydroxyde d'aluminium.

D.   Kaolin-Gruppe (f)
        Tonminerale, bei denen jede Silizium-Oxyd-Schicht mit
        einer Aluminium-Hydroxyd-Schicht verbunden (kondensiert)
        ist.

Esp.   grupo del caolín
        Minerales de arcilla en los cuales a cada capa de
        sílice y oxígeno corresponde una de hidróxido de
        aluminio.

P.   grupo do caolino
        Minerais das argilas em que para cada folha de silício-
        oxigénio ha uma de hidroxido de alumínio.

I.   gruppo (m) del caolino (m)
        Minerali delle argille in cui ogni strato di ioni
        silicio-ossigeno à collegato con uno strato costituito
        da idrossido d'alluminio.

Nl.   kaoliengroep
        Kleimineraal, waarin elke SiO_2 laag is verbonden met
        een aluminium-hydroxyde laag.

S.   kaolingruppens mineral
        Ej svällbara lermineral i vilka varje kiselsyreskikt
        är förenat med ett aluminiumhydroxidskikt.

242

Eng. isomorphous replacement
        Substitution of any atom in a crystal structure by an
        atom of approximately the same diameter.

F.   remplacement isomorphe
        Substitution d'un atome ou d'un ion par un autre à
        l'intérieur d'un réseau cristallin.

D.   isomorpher Ersatz
        Ersatz von einem Atom oder Ion durch ein anderes in
        einem Kristallgitter.

Esp. substitución isomórfica
        Cambio de un átomo por otro dentro del retículo del
        cristal.

P.   substituição isomorfa
        Substituição de um átomo por outro dentro de um reti-
        culado cristalino.

I.   sostituzione (f) isomorfa
        Sostituzione di un atomo da parte di un altro entro
        il reticolo di un cristallo.

Nl.   isomorfe vervanging
        Vervanging van een atoom door een ander binnen een
        kristalrooster.

S.   isomorf ersättning
        Ersättning av en atom eller jon med en annan i ett
        kristallgitter.

K8

Eng. "base-mineral index"
    Percentage of minerals with a density greater than 2.68
in the soil fraction 0.6-0.2 mm, including mica.
(Swedish term).

F. --------------------
    Pourcentage dans la fraction 0,6-0,2 mm du sol des
minéraux de densité supérieure à 2,68, y compris la
mica.

D. "Bas-Mineral-Index"
    Prozentsatz der Minerale von einer höheren Dichte als
2,68, einschliesslich Glimmer, in der Bodenfraktion von
0,6-0,2 mm.

Esp. --------------------
    Término sueco empleado para referirse al porcentaje de
minerales con una densidad superior a 2,68 en la fracción del suelo comprendida entre 0,6 y 0,2 mm, incluyendo la mica.

P. índice de bases minerais
    Percentagem de minerais, incluindo mica, de densidade
superior a 2,68 existentes na fracção do solo de diâmetro compreendido entre 0,6 e 0,2 mm. (Termo sueco.)

I. indice (m) base-minerale
    Percentuale della frazione di terreno da 0,6 a 0,2 mm
di minerali con densità superiore a 2,68, la mica compresa.

Nl. "bas-mineraal index"
    Percentage aan mineralen met inbegrip van mica met
soortelijk gewicht groter dan 2,68, in de fractie
0,6-0,2 mm.

S. bas-mineral-index
    Procent mineral med sp. v. större än 2,68 i mellan-
sanden, inklusive glimmer.

Eng. **layer-lattice structure**
    Repetitive arrangement of atoms and ions in crystalline
    material.

F. **structure réticulaire feuilletée**
    Arrangement régulier des atomes et des ions en couches
    parallèles.

D. **Schichtgitterstruktur** (f)
    Anordnung von Atomen and Ionen in einer Folge von
    Netzebenen.

Esp. **estructura reticular**
    Distribución de los átomos y las iones en capas.

P. **estrutura em rede (ou reticulada**
    Arranjo dos átomos em lâminas ou folhas.

I. **struttura** (f) **a reticolo** (m)
    Disposizione degli atomi e degli ioni in strati sottili
    nel materiale cristallino.

Nl. **roosterstructuur**
    Regelmatige rangschikking van atomen in een kristal.

S. **gitterstruktur**
    Atomernas och jonernas placering i ordnade skikt.

Section L

SOIL CLASSIFICATION, GENERAL

CLASSIFICATION DES SOLS, GENERALITES

CLASIFICACION GENERAL DE SUELOS

Eng. solum
>   The part of the earth's crust influenced by climate
>   and vegetation.

F. ------------
>   Partie de l'écorce terrestre influencée par le climat
>   et la végétation.

D. Boden (Gesamtboden) (m)
>   Der durch Klima, Vegetation und andere Bodenbildungs-
>   faktoren beeinflusste obere Teil des Bodenprofils (A
>   und B Horizont).

Esp. solum
>   La capa de la corteza terrestre sobre la que influyen
>   el clima y la vegetación.

P. solo
>   Parte da crosta terrestre influenciada pelo clima e
>   pelos organismos vivos.

I. suolo (dal latino solum)
>   Porzione della crosta terrestre esposta all'influenza
>   del clima e della vegetazione.

Nl. solum
>   Het gedeelte van de aardkorst dat door klimaat en
>   vegetatie is beinvloed.

S. jordmån
>   Den del av jordskorpan, som är påverkad av de av kli-
>   matet och vegetationen betingade processerna.

L2

Eng. ------------
>Soil as a material in regard to mechanical and chemical composition or geological origin.

F. -----------
>Sol considéré au point de vue de sa composition mécanique et chimique ou de son origine géologique.

D. Bodenart
>Einteilung der Böden nach ihrer Korngrössenzusammensetzung (nach ihrem Gehalt an Sand, Ton, Humus und Kalk).

Esp. -----------
>El suelo considerado desde el punto de vista de su composición mecánica y química o de su origen geológico.

P. -----------
>O solo, considerado apenas sob o ponto de vista da sua composição mecânica e química, ou quanto à sua origem geológica.

I. -----------
>Suolo come materiale riguardo alla sua composizione meccanica e chimica o alla sua origine geologica.

Nl. grondsoort
>Grond in den zin van materiaal met betrekking tot de mechanische en chemische samenstelling of de geologische oorsprong.

S. jordart
>Jord som material med hänsyn till mekanisk eller kemisk sammansättning eller geologiskt ursprung.

Eng. <u>pedalfer</u>
     Soil containing accumulations of iron and aluminium compounds.

F. <u>pedalfer</u>
     Sol renfermant du fer et de l'aluminium et ne présentant pas d'accumulation de calcaire.

D. <u>"Pedalfer"</u>
     Boden, dessen Eigenschaften besonders durch den Gehalt an Aluminium und Eisen bestimmt werden.

Esp. <u>"pedalfer"</u>
     Suelo que no presenta una zona de acumulación de carbonato de calcio.

P. <u>pedálfer</u>
     Solo que não possue acumulação de carbonato de cálcio.

I. <u>pedalfer</u> (m)
     Terreno che possiede ossidi di ferro e alluminio.

Nl. <u>pedalfer</u>
     Grond, waarin geen ophoping van calciumcarbonaat heeft plaats gehad.

S. <u>pedalfer</u>
     Jordmån utan anrikning av kalciumkarbonat.

L4

Eng. <u>pedocal</u>
Soil containing an accumulation of calcium carbonate.

F. <u>pedocal</u>
Sol présentant une accumulation de calcaire.

D. "<u>Pedocal</u>" (m)
Boden mit einer Kalzium-Karbonat-Anreicherung.

Esp. "<u>pedocal</u>"
Suelo que presenta una zona de acumulación de carbonato de calcio.

P. <u>pedocal</u>
Solo que possue acumulação de carbonato de cálcio.

I. <u>pedocal</u> (m)
Terreno che contiene un'accumulazione di carbonato di calcio.

Nl. <u>pedocal</u>
Grond, waarin accumulatie van calciumcarbonaat heeft plaats gehad.

S. <u>pedocal</u>
Jordmån med ett anrikningsskikt av kalciumkarbonat.

Eng.   <u>zonal soil</u>
       Soil having a profile which shows a dominant influence
       of climate and vegetation on its development.

F.   <u>sol zonal</u>
       Sol dont le profil est dû aux effets du climat.

D.   <u>zonaler Boden</u> (m), (klimatischer Boden) (m)
       Boden dessen Profilausbildung hauptsächlich durch das
       Klima bedingt ist.

Esp.   <u>suelo zonal</u>
       Suelo que presenta un perfil desarrollado por effectos
       del clima, la vegetación etc.

P.   <u>solo zonal</u>
       Solo com características bem desenvolvidas que reflec-
       tem a influência dos factores activos da génese do
       solo, clima e organismos vivos.

I.   <u>terreno</u> (m) <u>zonale</u>
       Terreno il cui profilo ha subito uno sviluppo deter-
       minato dal clima.

Nl.   <u>zonale grond</u>
       Grond, met een profielontwikkeling, die duidelijk de
       invloed van het klimaat weerspiegelt.

S.   <u>zonal jordmån</u>
       Jord, som i sin utbildning tydligt påverkats av kli-
       matet.

Eng. **intrazonal soil**
> Well developed soil whose morphology reflects the
> influence of some local factor of relief, parent
> material or age rather than of climate and vegetation.

F. **sol intrazonal**
> Sol dont les caractères ne dépendent que faiblement
> du ceux du climat de la région.

D. **intrazonaler Boden** (m)
> Boden, dessen Morphologie mehr den Einfluss eines
> lokalen Faktors (Relief, Ausgangsmaterial oder Alter)
> als den von Klima und Vegetation widerspeigelt.

Esp. **suelo intrazonal**
> Suelo bien desarrollado cuya morfología refleja la
> influencia de factores locales como relieve, roca
> madre o edad y no del clima o la vegetación.

P. **solo intrazonal**
> Solo cujo perfil reflecte a influência dominante de
> algum factor local, como o relevo, o material origi-
> nario ou a idade, no efeito normal do clima e da vege-
> tação.

I. **terreno** (m) **intrazonale**
> Terreno la cui morfologia riflette l'influenza di
> alcuni fattori locali del rilievo, della roccia madre
> o dell'età anziché del clima e della vegetazione.

Nl. **intrazonale grond**
> Grond waarvan de morfologie meer bepaald wordt door
> enige locale factor, als reliëf, moedermateriaal of
> tijd, dan door klimaat of vegetatie.

S. **intrazonal jordmån**
> Jordmån som delvis saknar den för platsen typiska och
> av klimatet utformade profilen.

Eng. azonal soil
>   Soil lacking a profile dominantly influenced by climate,
>   vegetation, etc.

F.   sol azonal
>   Sol dont le profil n'est pas dû aux effets du climat,
>   de la végétation, etc.

D.   azonaler Boden (m)
>   Boden dessen Profilausbildung nicht vornehmlich durch
>   das Klimat und die Vegetation bedingt ist.

Esp. suelo azonal
>   Suelo que carece de un perfil desarrollado por efectos
>   del clima, la vegetación etc.

P.   solo azonal
>   Solo sem perfil desenvolvido por acção do clima, vege-
>   tação, etc.

I.   terreno (m) azonale
>   Terreno che manca di un profilo sviluppato in conseguenza
>   del clima, della vegetazione, ecc.

Nl.   azonale grond
>   Grond nog zonder een door klimaat of plantengroei bein-
>   vloede profielontwikkeling.

S.   azonal jordmån
>   Jordmån som ej har den för platsen karakteristika under
>   inverkan av klimatet, vegetationen etc. utbildade pro-
>   filen.

Eng.   great soil group
   A taxonomic group of soils including one or more
   families.

F.   grand groupe de sols
   Groupe taxonomique de sols comprenant une ou plusieurs
   familles correspondant à un même processus d'évolution.

D.   "grosse Boden-Gruppe" (f)
   (Genetischer) Bodentyp.

Esp.   gran grupo de suelos
   Un grupo taxonómico de suelos incluyendo una o más
   familias.

P.   grande grupo de solos
   Grupo taxonómico de solos com características internas
   comuns e que inclui uma ou mais famílias.

I.   gruppo principale (m) di terreni (m p)
   Un raggruppamento di terreni a scopo di classificazione
   che comprende una o più famiglie.

Nl.   bodemgroep
   Een groep gronden, die een of meer families omvat.

S.   jordmånshuvudgrupp
   En grupp av jordmåner omfattande en eller flera
   familjer.

Eng. **family (soil)**
      A taxonomic grouping of similar soils intermediate
      between series and great soil group.

F.   **famille de sols**
      Groupement taxonomique de sols semblables.

D.   **Boden-Familie** (f)
      Eine in U.S.A. gebräuchliche Gruppeneinteilung ähnlicher
      Böden; entspricht in Deutschland der Unterteilung einer
      "grössen Boden-Gruppe", also eines genetischen Bodentyps
      (z.B. brauner Waldboden hoher Basensättigung).

Esp. **familia de suelos**
      Una agrupación taxonómica de suelos semejantes intermedia
      entre la serie y el gran grupo de suelos.

P.   **família de solos**
      Grupo taxonómico de solos com perfís semelhantes, com-
      posto de uma ou mais séries distintas.

I.   **famiglia** (f) **di terreni** (m p)
      Una aggruppamento di terreni per la classificazione.

Nl.   **bodemfamilie**
      Een groepering van op elkaar gelijkende gronden.

S.   **jordmånsfamilj**
      En taxonomisk grupp av likartade jordmåner.

Eng.　<u>type (soil)</u>
　　　　A group of soils having horizons similar in distinguish-
　　　　ing characteristics and arrangement, and developed from
　　　　a particular kind of parent material. The lowest unit
　　　　in the U.S. system of soil classification.

F.　　<u>sol type</u>
　　　　Profil de constitution idéale auquel se rattache un
　　　　ensemble de profils réels d'origine et d'aspect sem-
　　　　blables.

D.　　<u>"Bodenspezies"</u> (m)
　　　　Eine in U.S.A. gebräuchliche Untergliederung der "Boden-
　　　　serie" in der die Böden zusammengefasst werden, die sich
　　　　sowohl in Herkunft und Profil als auch in ihrer Textur
　　　　weitgehend ähneln.

Esp.　<u>tipo de suelo</u>
　　　　Grupo de suelos muy similares en su perfil y orígen.

P.　　<u>tipo de solo</u>
　　　　Grupo de solos com perfil e origem semelhantes.

I.　　<u>tipo</u> (m) <u>di terreno</u>
　　　　Un gruppo di terreni assai simili in intessitura, pro-
　　　　filo e genesi.

Nl.　<u>bodemtype</u>
　　　　Een groep gronden, die in textuur, profiel en oorsprong
　　　　sterk op elkaar gelijkend zijn.

S.　　<u>marktyp</u>
　　　　Jordar inom en serie med likartad textur.

Eng. <u>series</u> (soil)
> A group of soils having horizons similar in distinguish-
> ing characteristics and arrangement in the soil profile,
> except for the texture of the surface soil, and formed
> from the same parent material.

F. <u>série de sols</u>
> Groupe de sols différant seulement par la texture de
> l'horizon superficiel.

D. <u>Bodenserie</u> (f)
> Eine in U.S.A. gebräuchliche Untergliederung der "Boden-
> familie" innerhalb der sich die Böden nur in der Textur
> ihres oberen Horizont unterscheiden.

Esp. <u>serie de suelos</u>
> Un grupo de suelos que tienen horizontes análogos en
> cuanto a rasgos morfológicos y disposición en el perfil,
> provienen de la misma roca madre y difieren unicamente
> en la textura de la capa superficial.

P. <u>série de solos</u>
> Um grupo de solos que podem diferir apenas no textura
> da camada superficial.

I. <u>serie</u> (f) <u>di terreni</u> (m p)
> Un gruppo di terreni che differiscono solo per l'intes-
> situra del terreno superficiale.

Nl. <u>bodemserie</u>
> Een groep gronden die onderling alleen in de granulaire
> samenstelling van de bovengrond verschillen.   (U.S.A.
> term.)

S. <u>jordserie</u>
> En grupp av jordmåner som skiljer sig åt endast ifråga
> om texturen i matjorden.

Eng.   <u>phase</u>
      A subdivision of any class of any category in the U.S.
      system of soil classification, based on features impor-
      tant to soil use and management, but not significant in
      the natural landscape for native plants. Not a category
      in the U.S. system.

F.   <u>phase</u>
      Dernière catégorie de la classification des sols, basée
      sur des caractères importants pour l'agriculture.
      (Employé aux E.U.)

D.   <u>Phase</u> (f), (<u>Variante</u>)
      Kleinste Einheit bei der Einteilung der Böden, bei der
      ackerbauliche Gesichtspunkte zum Ausdruck kommen.

Esp.   <u>fase</u>
      La categoría más baja en la clasificación del suelo,
      basada en características importantes en cuanto al uso
      agricola. (De uso en EE.UU.)

P.   <u>fase</u>
      <u>variedade</u>
      A mais baixa categoria na classificação dos solos,
      baseada em aspectos de interesse para a agricultura como
      o relevo, a pedregosidade, a erosão acelerada, etc.

I.   <u>fase</u> (f)
      La più semplice categoria nella classificazione dei
      terreni, basata sui caratteri agronomici. (Non usato
      in Italia nel significato pedologico.)

Nl.   <u>phase</u>
      Bodemeenheid, onderverdeling van een bodemtype, alleen
      verschillend van andere phasen in stevigheid, diepte,
      enz. (U.S.A. term.)

S.   <u>fas</u>
      En klassificeringsenhet inom en typ som skiljer sig från
      andra faser endast ifråga om stenighet, djup etc.

Eng. **association (soil)**
  A group of soils, differing mainly in their degree of
  natural drainage, associated geographically on one
  relatively uniform parent material (U.K.).
  A group of defined and named taxonomic units regularly
  associated geographically in a defined proportional
  pattern (U.S.).

F. **association (de sols)**
  Sols se rencontrant ensemble dans une région donnée et
  presentant entre eux une certaine relation.

D. **"Assoziation"** (f)
  In einem gegeben Gebiet zusammen vorkommende Böden die
  untereinander eine gewisse Beziehung aufweisen.

Esp. **asociación**
  Suelo que aparecen juntos dentro de una región.

P. **associação**
  Solos com ou sem características comuns que aparecem
  juntos numa região.

I. **associazione** (f)
  Terreni ohc si trovano insieme entro una zona.

Nl. **associatie**
  Gronden, die samen in een streek vorkomen.

S.- **association**
  Jordmåner som förekommer tillsammans inom ett visst
  område.

Eng. catena
      A sequence of different soils usually from similar
      parent material but varying with relief and drainage.

F.   chaîne de sols
      Succession de sols différents ayant généralement même
      roche-mère mais variant selon le relief et le drainage.

D.   Catena (f)
      Eine Aufeinanderfolge von verschiedenen Böden, gewöhn-
      liche aus ähnlichem Ausgangsmaterial aber verschieden in
      Bezug auf Relief und Drainage.

Esp. catena
      Una sucesión de diferentes suelos provenientes general-
      mente de una roca madre semejante pero variando segun el
      relieve y el drenaje.

P.   catena
      Uma sequência de solos diferentes geralmente derivados
      de materiais originários similares mas variando com o
      relevo e a drenagem.

I.   catena (f)
      Una sequenza di vari terreni generalmente originati
      dalla stessa roccia madre ma che variano con il rilievo
      e con lo scolo delle acque.

Nl.   catena
      Een opeenvolging van verschillende gronden, gewoonlijk
      gevormd uit hetzelfde moedermateriaal, maar wisselend
      van aard naar gelang van het reliëf en de afwatering.

S.   catena
      En serie jordar härrörande från samma ursprungsmaterial
      men differentierade av de topografiska och hydrologiska
      förhållandena.

ORGANIC AND PEAT SOILS

SOLS ORGANIQUES ET SOLS TOURBEUX

SUELOS ORGANICOS Y TURBOSOS

Eng. <u>**raised moss**</u>
<u>raised bog, (highmoor)</u>
    Peaty land consisting mainly of sphagnum.

F. <u>tourbe haute</u>
    Tourbe acide dont la surface se maintient au-dessus du
    niveau de l'eau.

D. <u>Hochmoor</u>
    Nährstoffarmes, meist aus Sphagneen bestehendes Moor,
    die ihren Wasserbedarf aus den Niederschlägen decken.

Esp. <u>turbera alta</u>
    Terreno turboso formado principalmente por <u>Sphagnum</u>.

P. <u>terreno pantanoso elevado</u>
    Terra turfosa ocupada principalmente por "sphagnum".

I. <u>torbiera (f) alta</u>
    Torbiera costituita principalmente de sfagni ed Erio-
    phorium.

Nl. <u>eutrooph veen</u>
    Veen gegroeid in een milieu met voedalsarm water.

S. <u>mosse</u>
    Ombrogen del av myr med speciell vegetation betingad
    av isolering från fastmarksvatten.

M₂

Eng.   <u>transitional moor</u>
   Moor intermediate in character between raised moss and
   low moor.

F.   <u>tourbière de transition</u>
   Formation marécageux, intermédiaire entre tourbières
   hautes et tourbières basses.

D.   <u>Übergangsmoor</u>
   Zwischen Niederungs- und Hochmoor stehende Moorbildung.

Esp.   <u>turbera de transición</u>
   Formación intermedia entre turbera alta y turbera
   sumergida.

P.   <u>pântano de transição</u>
   Pântano de carácter intermediário entre o pântano elevado e o pântano baixo.

I.   <u>torbiera (f) di transizione</u>
   Formazione paludosa, intermedia tra torbiere a sfagno
   e terre di pianura.

Nl.   <u>mesotrooph veen</u>
   Veen hetwelk eigenschappen vertoont tussen oligotrooph
   veen en eutrooph veen.

S.   <u>fattigkärr</u>
   Kärr med artfattig vegetation.

Eng. <u>fen soil</u>
<u>lowmoor</u>
Peaty land formed in low-lying positions under anaerobic
conditions and containing much sedimentary material.

F. <u>tourbière basse</u>
Marais dans lequel se produit la décomposition des
matières végétales an anaérobiose.

D. <u>Niederungsmoor</u> (n)
Durch Verlandung unter Zufluss nährstoffreichen Wassers
entstandenes Moor.

Esp. <u>turbera sumergida</u>
Primer estado del marjal formado en una depresión.

P. <u>brejo turfoso</u>
Início de um paúl formado numa depressão.

I. <u>torbiera</u> (f) <u>bassa</u>
Terra torbosa, generalmente neutra o alcalina, sotto-
posta a decomposizione anaerobica.

Nl. <u>laagveenmoeras</u>
Een vroeg stadium van een moeras, dat gevormd is in een
laagte.

S. <u>kärr</u>
Myr eller del därav med artrikare vegetation och närings-
rikare torv än mossen beroende på tillflöde av fastmarks-
vatten.

M4

Eng. <u>Bog soil</u>
Peaty soil with surface peat deeper than about 16 cm
formed under poorly drained conditions.

F. <u>Sol Tourbeux</u>
Sol humifère formé dans les marécages, sous climat
humide ou subhumide.

D. <u>Moorboden</u>
Boden mit mehr als 30% organischem Substanz.

Esp. <u>suelo turboso</u>
Suelo orgánico, formado en pantanos, de climas húmedos
o sub-húmedos.

P. <u>solo turfoso</u>
Solo de turfa formado nos charcos dos climas húmidos
e sub-húmidos.

I. <u>terreno (m) torboso</u>
Terreno torboso formato nelle paludi in climi umidi e
subumidi.

Nl. <u>veengrond</u>
Venige grond gevormd in moerassen in een subhumied of
humied klimaat.

S. <u>torvjord</u>
Jord bildad i myrar i humitt eller subhumitt klimat.

Eng.   Half Bog soil
        Swampy or marshy soil with an organic horizon overlying
        gray mineral soil.

F.   ------------
        Sol présantant un horizon organique reposant sur un sous-
        sol gris non humifère.

D.   anmooriger Boden
        Mineralboden mit hohem Gehalt an organischem Substanz
        (15-30%).

Esp.   suelo semipantanoso (semicenagoso)
        Suelo con un horizonte orgánico que descansa sobre un
        suelo mineral gris.

P.   solo Semi-pantanoso
        Solo de zonas mal drenadas com um horizonte orgânico
        assente em matéria mineral cinzenta.

T.   -------------
        Terreno con un orizzonte organico sovrastante terreno
        mineral grigio.

Nl.   Venige grond
        Grond met een dunne venige horizont op een grijze
        minerale grond.

S.   gråblå sumpjordmån
        Gråblå jord med mycket högt grundvattenstånd täckt av
        ett relativt tunt torvskikt.

Eng. <u>tundra</u>
   Treeless, mossy and partly marshy plain of arctic
   regions.

F. <u>toundra</u>
   Plaine des régions arctiques sans arbre, moussue et
   en partie marécageuse.

D. <u>Tundra</u> (f)
   Baumlose, moosbewachsene und zum Teil sumpfige Ebene
   arktischer Gebiete.

Esp. <u>tundra</u>
   Llanura sin árboles, musgosa, parcialmente cenagosa,
   de las regiones árticas.

P. <u>tundra</u>
   Planície das regiões árticas, sem árvores, coberta de
   musgos, em parte pantanosa e com substrato permanentemente gelado.

I. <u>tundra</u> (f)
   Pianure delle regioni artiche sensa alberi con (pre-
   valente vegetazione di) muschi, (e licheni) e in parte
   impaludate.

Nl. <u>toendra</u>
   Boomloze, bemoste en gedeeltelijk moerassige vlakte in
   arctische streken.

S. <u>tundra</u>
   Trädlöst, mossbevuxet och delvis sumpigt slättområde i
   arktiska regioner.

Eng. <u>tundra soil</u>
Dark coloured soil with highly organic surface horizon
and a frozen subsoil.

F. <u>sol de toundra</u>
Sol présentant des horizons organiques et minéraux et
un sous-sol gelé.

D. <u>Tundraboden</u>
Boden mit organischen und mineralischen Horizonten und
gefrorenem Untergrund.

Esp. <u>suelo de tundra</u>
Suelo con horizontes orgánicos y minerales y un subsuelo
helado.

P. <u>solo tundra</u>
Solo com material orgânico e mineral e um subsolo permanentemente gelado.

I. <u>terreno</u> (m) <u>di tundra</u> (f)
Terreno con orizzonti organici e minerali e il sottosuolo (permanentemente) ghiacciato.

Nl. <u>toendragrond</u>
Grond met humeuze en minerale horizonten en een bevroren
ondergrond.

S. <u>tundrajord</u>
Den subarktiska klimatzonens jordmån. Utmärkes av övervägande fysikalisk (mekanisk) vittring, vattendränkning
och på visst djup permanent tjäle.

Eng. **swamp**
    Wet spongy ground.

F. **marais**
    Sol spongieux humide.

D. **Sumpf**
    Nasser schwammiger Grund.

Esp. **pantano**
    Terreno esponjoso mojado.

P. **pântano**
    Terreno húmido esponjoso.

I. **pantano** (m)
    palude (f)
    Terreno umido.

Nl. **moeras**
    Nat terrein met slechte afwatering.

S. **sumpmark**
    Vattengenomdränkt organogen mark.

Eng. **gyttja**
Name for humic soils of sedimentary origin in which the humus consists mainly of plant and animal residues precipitated from standing water (gyttja substance).

F. ------------
Sols humiques d'origine sédimentaire, dont l'humus est composé des résidus végétaux et animaux qui se precipitent des eaux stagnantes riches en principes nutritifs.

D. **Gyttja** (f)
In nährstoffreichem Wasser abgesetzte, pflanzliche und tierische Bestandteile enthaltende, Mudde.

Esp. **gyttja**
Nombre que se aplica a suelos orgánicos en los cuales el humus proviene principalmente de residuos vegetales y animales precipitados del agua estancada.

P. **"gyttja"**
Solo húmico de origem sedimentar, cujo húmus é fundamentalmente constituido por resíduos vegetais e animais precipitados de águas estagnadas (substância "gyttja").

I. ------------
Terreni umici di sedimenti, con umus composto di residui vegetali e animali precipitata in acque stagnanti ricche in elementi nutritivi.

Nl. **gyttja**
Benaming voor humusrijke gronden van limnische en sedimentaire oorsprong, waarvan de humus hoofdzakelijk uit plantaardige en dierlijke, in stilstaand water afgezette overblijfselen bestaat.

S. **gyttja**
Samlingsnamn för limniska, sedimentära humusjordar, i vilka humusen till övervägande delen utgöres av gyttjesubstans.

M10

Eng. **dy**

Muddy material formed of plant residues and deposited from nutrient-poor water.

F. ------------

Matière bourbeuse, composée des résidus végétaux et déposée des eaux pauvres ęn principes nutritifs.

D. **Dy** (m)

In nährstoffarmem Wasser abgesetzte, nur pflanzliche Substanz enthaltende Mudde.

Esp. ------------

Depósito cenagoso formado por residuos de plantas desarrolladas en aguas pobres en elementos nutritivos.

P. **"dy"**

Material lodoso constituido por resíduos vegetais e depositado de águas pobres em elementos nutritivos.

I. ------------

Sostanza fangosa, composta di residui vegetali e deposta delle acque scarse d'elementi nutritivi.

Nl. **dy**

Uit plantaardige overblijfselen gevormde modder, afgezet uit water arm aan voedingsstoffen.

S. **dy**

En av utfällda humusämnen bestående strukturlös, vanligen mörkfärgad massa.

Eng. ------------
Calcareous recent marine sediments occurring along the
North Sea coast.

F. ------------
Sédiments marins actuels renfermant du calcaire et se
rencontrant le long du littoral de la Mer du Nord.

D. Seemarsch
Kalkhaltige rezente Meeressedimente im Küstenbereich
der Nordsee.

Esp. ------------
Sedimentos marinos de origen reciente, de naturaleza
calcárea que aparecen a lo largo de la costa del Mar
del Norte.

P. ------------
Sedimentos calcáreos modernos de origem marinha que
aparecem nas costas do Mar do Norte.

I. ------------
Sedimenti marini recenti che contengono calce e si
trovano lungo la costa del Mare del Nord.

Nl. schor
kwelder
gors
Begroeide kalkhoudende recente sedimenten uit zee
welke zich langs de kust van de Noordzee bevinden.

S. marsk
Recenta marina sediment vid en tidvattenskust.

Eng. -----------
Higher-lying area of Pleistocene origin, usually with light soils, adjoining a marsh on the landward side.

F. -----------
Haut terrain d'origine Pleistocene, généralement occupé par des sols légers avoisinant une tourbière du côté d l'intérieur.

D. Geest (f)
Landeinwärts an die Marsch anschliessendes höher gelegenes Gebiet Pleistozäner Herkunft mit meist leichten Böden.

Esp. -----------
Tierra de origen Pleistoceno, generalmente con suelos ligeros, y adyacente a un pantano.

P. -----------
Àrea de cota elevada de origem pleistocénica, geralmente com solos ligeiros, junto dum pântano.

I. -----------
Piana ad una certa altitudine d'origine pleistocenica, con terreni ordinariamente leggeri ed adiacenti alle terre paludose.

Nl. garst-, gast(gronden)
Een landwaarts aan een zeekleigebied grenzend, hoger liggend gebied van Pleistocene oorsprong, hoofdzakelijk bestaande uit lichte gronden.
geest
Een vochtige duinzandgrond, die soms iets kleihoudend is.

S. -----------
Högre belägen mark på landsidan av marsk. Av pleistocent ursprung och i regel bestående av lättare jordarter.

Eng. <u>older peat</u>
      Old, highly decomposed peat of raised moss.

F. -----------
      Tourbe ancienne de tourbes hautes, de décomposition
      avancée.

D. <u>Schwarztorf</u>
      Älterer Hochmoortorf mit hohem Zersetzungsgrad.

Esp. -----------
      Turba antigua, producida por turbera alta y altamente
      descompuesta.

P. <u>turfa antiga</u>
      Turfa antiga, muito decomposta, dos pântanos elevados.

I. <u>torba (f) vecchia</u>
      Torba vecchia di sfagno, di decomposizione avanzata.

Nl. <u>zwarte turf</u>
      Oud, sterk verteerd hoogveen.

S. -----------
      Höghumifierad vitmosstorv.

M14

Eng. <u>younger peat</u>
Young, slightly decomposed peat of raised moss.

F. ------------
Tourbe récente de **plateaux**, peu décomposée.

D. <u>Weisstorf</u> (m)
Jüngerer Hochmoortorf von geringem Zersetzungsgrad.

Esp. <u>turba reciente</u>
Turba de turberas altas, ligeramente descompuesta.

P. <u>turfa recente</u>
Turfa recente, ligeiramente decomposta, dos pântanos
elevados.

I. <u>torba giovane</u>
Torba recente di sfagno, leggermente decomposta.

Nl. <u>witte turf</u>
Jong, weinig verteerd hoogveen.

S. ------------
Låghumifierad vitmosstorv.

Eng. <u>recurrence horizon</u>
  Thin layer between the older and younger horizons of
  raised bogs.

F. ------------
  Couche mince entre l'horizon ancien et récent des
  tourbières à sphaignes.

D. <u>Grenzhorizont</u> (m)
  Dünne Schicht zwischen Schwarztorf und Weisstorf in
  Hochmooren.

Esp. ------------
  Capa delgada entre los horizontes antiguos y los nuevos
  en una turbera alta.

P. ------------
  Camada delgada entre os horizontes antigos e recentes
  dos pântanos elevados.

I. ------------
  Strato sottile fra l'orizzonte antico e recente delle
  torbiere a sfagno.

Nl. <u>grenslaag van Weber</u>
  Dunne laag tussen zwarte en witte turf in hoogveen.

S. <u>rekurrensyta</u>
  Klimatiskt betingad gränsyta, mellan hög- och låghumifierad torv, pollenanalytiskt och i regel även mor-
  fologiskt påvisbar.

Eng. <u>peat clay</u>
<u>organic silt</u>
The lowest layer of a moor in which mineral and organic
constituents are mixed.

F. ------------
Couche la plus profonde d'un marais dans laquelle les
éléments minéraux et organiques se trouvent mélangés.

D. <u>Mudde</u> (f)
Unterste Schicht eines Moores, in der mineralische und
organische Bestandteile vermischt sind (Sapropel, Faul-
schlamm).

Esp. <u>limo organico</u>
La capa inferior de una turbera en la cual los consti-
tuyentes minerales y orgánicos aparecen mezclados.

P. <u>turfa argilosa</u>
<u>limo orgânico</u>
A camada inferior dum terreno pantanoso onde os consti-
tuintes minerais e orgânicos se encontram misturados.

I. <u>argilla</u> (f) <u>torbosa</u>
<u>limo</u> (m) <u>organico</u>
Lo strato più profondo d'una palude nel quale i
materiali minerali e organici si trovano mescolati.

Nl. <u>sapropeel</u>
De onderste laag van een veen waarin de minerale en
organische bestanddelen zijn vermengd.

S. ------------
Understa skiktet i en myr, där mineral- och organogena
beståndsdelar sammanblandats.

Eng. <u>tirr</u>
The loose, slightly decomposed, uppermost layer of a
raised moss.

F. ------------
Couche supérieure, meuble et peu décomposée, d'une
tourbière à sphaignes.

D. <u>Bunkerde</u>
Oberste, lockere, wenig zersetzte Schicht eines Hoch-
moores.

Esp. ------------
La capa superior de una turbera alta, poco descompuesta.

P. ------------
A camada superior, sôlta e ligeiramente decomposta, dum
pântano elevado.

I. ------------
Strato superiore, sciolto e poco decomposto d'una
torbiera a sfagno.

Nl. <u>bonkaarde</u>
De bovenste, losse, weinig verteerde laag van een hoogveen.

S. ------------
Det lösa, måttligt förmultnade översta lagret i en mosse.

Eng. ------------
   Calcareous material obtained from underneath marsh soils
   and used for the amelioration of heavy marsh soils.

F. -----------
   Matière calcaire obtenue de la couche de dessous des
   sols marécageux, appliquée à l'amélioration des tourbières lourdes.

D. Blausand
   Püttsand
   Kuhlerde
   Kalkhaltiges Material aus dem Untergrund der Marschböden,
   das zur Melioration der schweren Marschen verwendet wird.

Esp. ------------
   Material calcáreo obtenido del interior de suelos pantanosos y que a veces se usa como enmienda para dichos suelos.

P. -----------
   Material calcário extraido de camadas existentes sob
   solos pantanosos e usado na correcção destes.

I. "sabbia azzurra" (f)
   Sostanza calcarea che si ottiene di al disotto delle terre
   paludose, per il miglioramento delle torbiere pesanti.

Nl. blauw zand
   Kalkhoudend materiaal dat gevonden wordt onder zeeklei-
   gronden en benut wordt om deze te verbeteren.

S. ------------
   Kalkhaltig alv från vissa marskjordar; användes som jord-
   förbättringsmedel på styva marskjordar.

Eng. ------------
          Compacted layer in marshland.

F. ------------
          Couche compacte des sols marécageux.

D. <u>Knickschicht</u> (f)
          Verdichtungsschicht in Marschböden.

Esp. ------------
          Capa compacta de tierras pantanosas.

P. ------------
          Camada compacta das terras pantanosas.

I. ------------
          Strato compatto delle terre paludose.

Nl. <u>kniklaag</u>
    <u>kniplaag</u>
          Een compacte laag in zeeklei.

S. ------------
          Förtätat skikt i marskjordar.

M20

Eng. ------------
Iron-sulphide-containing material which occurs in the
deeper layers of marshy soils and yields plant-poisonous
substances on exposure to air.

F. ------------
Matière se trouvant dans les couches plus profondes des
sols marécageux dont les sulfures de fer, exposés a l'air,
produisent des substances phytotoxiques.

D. Pulvererde
Maibolt
In den tieferen Schichten des Marschbodens vorkommendes
Material, in dem — wegen des Gehaltes an Schwefeleisen
— bei Luftzutritt pflanzengiftige Stoffe entstehen.

Esp. ------------
Dícese de los materiales contentivos de sulfuro de hierro
que aparecen en las capas profundas de suelos pantanosos
que producen substancias venenosas para las plantas al
ponerse en contacto con el aire.

P. ------------
Material com sulfureto de ferro que aparece nas camadas
mais fundas dos solos pantanosos e que dá origem a sub-
stâncias tóxicas para as plantas quando exposto ao ar.

I. ------------
Solfuri di ferro con sostanza che si trova negli strati
più profondi delle terre paludose la quale, esposta
all'aria, produce delle materie fitotossiche.

Nl. katte-klei
Zwavelijzer bevattend materiaal dat in de diepere lagen
van brakwater-gronden wordt gevonden en dat bij bloot-
stelling aan de lucht voor de planten giftige bestanddelen produceert.

S. ------------
Järnsulfidhaltigt material, som förekommer i de djupare
lagren av marskjordar, och som vid lufttillträde oxideras
till för växterna giftiga föreningar.

Section N

PODZOLIC SOILS

SOLS PODZOLIQUES

SUELOS PODSOLICOS

Eng. Brown earth
      Brown Forest soil
          Soil with mull horizon and having no accumulation hori-
          zon of clay and sesquioxides.

F.   Sol Brun
      Terre Brune
          Sol présentant un horizon d'humus doux mais pas d'accumu-
          lation en profondeur d'argile ou de sesquioxydes.

D.   Braunerde (f)
      brauner Waldboden (m)
          Boden (des gemässigten humiden Klimas) mit Mullhorizont
          und geringem Auswaschungsgrad, der keine Verlagerungen
          von Ton oder Sesquioxyden aufweist (A-(B)-C Profil).

Esp. suelo pardo forestal
          Suelo con un horizonte de humus dulce y que no tiene un
          zona de acumulación de arcilla o sesquióxidos.

P.   Terra Parda
      solo Pardo Florestal
          Solo com horizontes superficiais ricos em humus doce e
          sem horizonte de acumulação de argila ou sesquióxidos.

I.   terra bruna (f)
      terreno (m) forestale bruno
          Terreno con orizzonte ricco di sostanza organica ben
          decomposta in gran parte transformata in umus, a strut-
          tura granulare, a reazione subacida o leggermente alca-
          lina, senza accumulo di argilla e di sesquiossidi.

Nl.   Bruine grond
      Bruine bosgrond
          Grond met een milde humuslaag en zonder ophoping van
          klei of sesquioxyden in de diepere horizonten.

S.   brunjord
      brun skogsjord
          Podsolisk jordmån utan A$_2$, med ett relativt mäktigt mull-
          skikt vilande på ett brunt skikt innehållande ler och
          seskvioxider.

Eng. <u>Podzol</u>
Soil with acid-humus horizon overlying B horizon of iron-oxide or iron-oxide and humus accumulation.

F. <u>Podzol</u>
Sol caractérisé par un horizon très clair, à structure cendreuse ou lamellaire, surmonté d'horizons humifères acides et reposant sur des horizons d'accumulation en général enrichis en fer et en argile et souvent en humus.

D. <u>Podsol</u> (m), <u>(Bleicherde)</u> (f)
Boden mit saurem Humus (Rohhumusauflage), gebleichtem A_2-Horizont und typischem Anreicherungshorizont.

Esp. <u>suelo podsol</u>
Suelo con humus ácido encima de un horizonte descolorido que descansa a su vez sobre un horizonte de acumulación de hierro.

P. <u>Podzol</u>
Solo caracterizado por uma camada orgânica e outra orgânico-mineral (ambas com húmus ácido) sobre um horizonte cinzento de lavagem que assenta num de acumulação de ferro, alumina e às vezes de matéria orgânica.

I. <u>podsolo</u> (m)
Terreno con umus acido, ricoprente un orizzonte sbiancato, sovrastante a sua volta ad un orizzonte con accumulazione di composti del ferro e umus.

N1. <u>podzol</u>
Grond met een dek van zure humus, een uitgeloogde horizont en een inspoelings-horizont bestaande uit humus en sesquioxyden.

S. <u>podsol</u>
Jordmån med ett skikt av sur humus (råhumus) överlagrande ett utlakat skikt, under vilket följer ett anrikningsskikt med seskvioxider, ibland med tydlig humusavlagring i de översta delarna.

Eng. <u>Brown Podzolic soil</u>
Acid soil developed under forest with little or no
bleached A_2 horizon and only a weak texture profile.
Organic matter, sesquioxides and clay decrease gradual-
ly with depth.

F. <u>Sol Brun Podzolique</u>
<u>Sol Podzolique peu évolué</u>
Sol ayant des horizons A_0 et A_1 peu épais; un horizon A_2 blanchi et très mince; et un horizon B brun
et plus lourd.

D. <u>podsolige Braunerde</u> (f)
<u>podsoliger brauner Waldboden</u> (m)
Boden mit dünnem A_0 und A_1, sehr dünnem gebleichtem A_2
und braunem schwererem B-Horizont; Übergang vom
braunen Waldboden geringer Basensättigung zum Podsol.

Esp. <u>suelo podsólico pardo</u>
Suelo con horizontes A_0 y A_1 de poco espesor, el horizonte A_2 muy ligeramente descolorido y el B pardo más
pesado.

P. <u>solo Pardo Podzolisado</u>
Solo com os horizontes A_0 et A_1 delgados, A_2 lavado,
cinzento claro e muito delgado e B pardo ou pardo-
amarelado, de textura máis pesada que a do solo superficial.

I. <u>terra</u> (f) <u>podsolica bruna</u>
Terreno con gli orizzonti A_0 e A_1 fini, l'orizzonte A_2
molto fine e sbiancato, l'orizzonte B marrone e più
compatto.

Nl. <u>Bruine podzolgrond</u>
Grond met een dunne A_0 en A_1, een zeer dunne, zwak
uitgeloogde A_2 en een bruine, verdichte B-horizont.

S. <u>podsolartad brunjord</u>
Jord med ett tunt A_0- och A_1-, mycket tunt blekt A_2-
och ett brunt tjockare B-skikt.

Eng. <u>Gray Brown Podzolic soil</u>
Forest soil with thin A_0 and A_1 over a grayish brown leached A_2 and brown blocky B horizon.

F. <u>Sol Brun Lessivé</u>
Sol ayant des horizons A_0 et A_1 peu épais, au-dessus d'un horizon lessivé A_2, brun grisâtre ou beige; et un horizon B brun.

D. <u>stark podsoliger brauner Waldboden</u> (m)
Waldboden mit dünnem A_0 and A_1, über grau-braunem gebleichten A_2 und braunem B-Horizont.

Esp. <u>suelo podsólico pardo grisáceo</u>
Suelo con horizontes A_0 y A_1 delgados sobre un A_2 pardo grisáceo lixiviado y un B pardo.

P. <u>solo Pardo-acinzentado Podzolizado</u>
Solo com horizontes A_0 e A_1 relativamente delgados sobre um horizonte A_2 pardo-acinzentado lavado, assente, por sua vez, num horizonte pardo iluvial.

I. <u>terra (f) podsolica bruna grigia</u>
Terreno con gli orizzonti A_0 e A_1 soprastanti un orizzonte A_2 bruno grigio liscíviato e un orizzonte B bruno.

Nl. <u>Grijsbruine podzolgrond</u>
Grond met een dunne A_0 en A_1 op een grijsbruin gebleekte A_2 en een bruine B horizont.

S. <u>gråbrun podsolisk jordmån</u>
Jord med ett tunt A_0- och A_1-skikt över ett gråbrunt urlakat A_2- och ett brunt kompakt B-skikt.

Eng.   Gray Wooded soil
      Soil with thin A_1, thick gray A_2 and grayish brown
      blocky B horizons, commonly over calcareous parent
      material.

F.   Sol Gris Forestier
      Sol ayant des horizons A_0 et A_1 peu épais et blanchi,
      et un horizon B, brun et plus lourd.

D.   podsolierter (grauer) Boden (m)
      Boden mit dünnem A_0 und A_1, starkem, gebleichtem A_2
      und braunem B-Horizont.

Esp.   suelo gris de bosque
      Suelo con horizonte A_1 delgado, A_2 profundo, horizonte
      B castaño grisáceo, comunmente derivado de material
      calcáreo.

P.   solo Cinzento florestal
      Solo com A_0 e A_1 delgados, A_2 muito lavado e B pardo
      e de textura mais fina.

I.   terreno (m) grigio forestale
      Terreno con gli orizzonti A_0 e A_1 di notevole spessore,
      l'orizzonte A_2 sbiancato e l'orizzonte B più compatto
      e bruno ruggine.

Nl.   Grijze bosgrond
      Grond met een dunne A_0 en A_1, een dikke gebleekte A_2 en
      een bruine zwaardere B horizont.

S.   grå skogsjord
      Grå, något podsolerad jord med obetydligt A_0- och A_1-
      skikt, djupt blekt A_2- och brunt kompakt B-skikt.

Eng. <u>ground-water podzol</u>
Intrazonal great soil group including imperfectly drained sandy soils with very thin A_1 horizons, prominent white A_2 horizons, and hard or compact dark brown B horizons.

F. <u>podzol de nappe</u>
Podzol situé sur matériau sableux présentant une nappe phréatique à faible profondeur.

D. <u>Grundwassergleipodsol</u> (m)
Podsol mit hohem Grundwasserstand.

Esp. <u>podsol hidromórfico</u>
Podsol que se encuentra en arena pobremente drenada.

P. <u>podzol hidromórfico</u>
Podzol desenvolvido a partir de depósitos arenosos de imperfeita drenagem.

I. <u>podsolo</u> (m) <u>determinato da una falda</u> (f) <u>freatica</u>
Podsolo che si trova in sabbia a scolo deficiente.

Nl. <u>grondwater-podzol</u>
Podzol dat men vindt in slecht ontwaterd zandgrond.

S. <u>grundvattenpodsol</u>
Podsol som uppkommer på jord med högt grundvattenstånd.

Eng. Red Podzolic soil
        Soil with thin A_O and A_1, yellowish brown to nearly
        white leached A_2 and red B horizons.

F.   Sol Rouge Podzolique
        Sol formé par des processus intenses de décomposition
        de la roche mère, présentant un horizon humifère peu
        épais, un horizon lessivé brun-jaunâtre, au-dessus
        d'un horizon d'accumulation rouge. (Non utilisé en
        français.)

D.   roter podsoliger Boden
        Boden mit dünnem A_O- und A_1-, gelblich-braunem bis
        fast weissem gebleichtem A_2- und rotem B-Horizont.

Esp. suelo podsólico rojo
        Suelo con horizontes A_O y A_1 de poco espesor, el
        horizonte A_2 pardo amarillento lixiviado y el B rojo.

P.   solo Vermelho Podzolizado
        Solo com horizontes A_O e A_1 delgados, A_2 pardo
        amarelado, lavado e B vermelho.

I.   terra (f) podsolica rossa
        Terreno con gli orizzonti A_O e A_1, di poco spessore,
        l'orizzonte A_2 bruno giallognolo quasi bianco lisci-
        viato e l'orizzonte B rosso.

Nl.   Rode podzolgrond
        Grond met een dunne A_O en A_1, een geelbruin gebleekte
        A_2 en een rode B horizont.

S.   röd podsolisk jord
        Jord med ett tunt A_O- och A_1-skikt och ett gulbrunt
        urlakat A_2- samt rött B-skikt.

Eng. <u>Yellow Podzolic soils</u>
A group of well developed, well drained acid soils having thin A_0 and organic-mineral A_1 horizons over a light coloured, bleached A_2 horizon over a red, yellowish-red, or yellow and more clayey B horizon. Coarse streaks or mottles of red, yellow, brown, and light gray characterize deep horizons where the siliceous parent materials are thick.

F. <u>Sols Jaunes Podzoliques</u>
Groupe de sols acides, bien développés bien drainés, ayant un horizon A_0 mince, un horizon organo-minéral A_1, légèrement coloré, un horizon A_2 blanchi au-dessus d'un horizon B plus argileux, rouge, rouge jaunâtre ou jaune. Des trainées ou des taches rouges, jaunes, brunes ou gris clair caractérisent les horizons profonds constitués par des roches-mères siliceuses épaisses. (Non utilisé en français.)

D. <u>gelbe, podsolige Böden</u> (m p)
Eine Gruppe gut entwickelter, durchlässiger, saurer Böden mit dünnem A_0-, organisch-mineralischem A_1-, und schwach gefärbtem, gebleichtem A_2-Horizont über rötlichem oder gelblichem, tonigerem B-Horizont. Unregelmässige rote, gelbe, braune bzw. hellgraue Streifen oder Flecken kennzeichnen die unteren Horizonte, die stark mit silikatischem Ausgangsmaterial durchsetzt sind.

Esp. <u>suelos amarillos podsólicos</u>
Grupo de suelos ácidos bien desarrollados y bien drenados, que tienen una capa delgada A_0 y un horizonte A_1 organico-mineral ligeramente coloreado. El horizonte A_2, blancuzco descansa sobre un horizonte B, más arcilloso rojizo, rojo-amarillento o amarillo. Los horizontes profundos, formados por material parental silícico, son gruesos y se caracterizan por la presencia de concreciones rojizas, rojo-amarillentas o ligeramente grises.

P. **solos Amarelos Podzolizados**
    Grupo de solos bem desenvolvidos, ácidos e bem drenados,
    com o horizonte A_0 delgado, A_1 orgânico-mineral, A_2 de
    côr clara ou esbranquiçado e B vermelho, vermelho-
    amarelado ou amarelo mais argiloso que o anterior. Nos
    horizontes inferiores dos solos derivados de materiais
    originários siliciosos e espessos aparecem faixas ou
    manchas mosqueadas de vermelho, amarelo, cinzento claro
    e de textura grosseira.

I. **terreni (m p) gialli pozzolici**
    Un gruppo di terreni acidi bene sviluppati e ben drenati
    aventi un orizzonte A_0 e un orizzonte A_1 organico-
    minerale sopra un orizzonte A_2 debolmente colorato,
    sbiancato, sopra un orizzonte B rosso, rosso giallastro,
    o giallo più argilloso. Strisce grossolane o pomellature
    di rosso, giallo, marrone, e leggermente grige caratteriz-
    zano gli orizzonti profondi dove la roccia madre silicea
    è spessa.

N1. **Gele podzolgronden**
    Een groep goed ontwikkelde, goed ontwaterende zure grond-
    en met een dunne A_0 en een uit organisch en mineraal
    materiaal bestaande A_1 horizont, een licht gekleurde,
    gebleekte A_2 horizont, een rode, geelrode of gele,
    zwaardere B horizont. Brede strepen of grote vlekken
    van een rode, gele, bruine of lichtgrijze kleur zijn
    typerend voor diepe horizonten waar het silicaatrijke
    moedermateriaal dik is.

S. **gula podsoljordar**
    En grupp av väl utvecklade, väldränerade sura jordmåner,
    med ett tunt A_0-skikt och ett organisktmineraliskt A_1-
    skikt över ett ljusfärgat blekt A_2-skikt underlagrat av
    ett rött, gulrött eller gult lerigare B-skikt. Grova
    ränder eller fläcker i rött, gult, brunt eller ljusgrått
    karakterisera de djupare skikten i de fall, då det kisel-
    rika modermaterialet bildar djupare lager.

Section O

GLEY AND MEADOW SOILS

SOLS DE GLEY ET SOLS DE PRAIRIES

SUELOS DE GLEY Y DE PRADERA

Eng. Wiesenboden
wet meadow soil
Poorly drained soil with humus-rich A_1 horizon grading
into gray gleyed mineral soil. Now included in humic-
gley soils.

F. Sol de Prairie
Sol dont la partie supérieure, très organique, passe
progressivement à des horizons gris peu humifères.

D. Wiesenboden (m)
Boden mit relativ hohem Grundwasserstand und stark
organischem Oberboden der in grauen Mineralboden über-
geht.

Esp. Wiesenboden
Suelo altamente orgánico en la capa arable que pasa
gradualmente a un suelo mineral de color gris.

P. "Wiesenboden"
solo dos Prados Naturais
Solo rico em matéria orgânica à superfície e passando
gradualmente a uma camada mineral cinzenta.

I. Wiesenboden
Terreno minerale con scarso drenaggio e lo strato super-
ficiale molto ricco in sostanza organica sovrapposto a
terreno minerale grigio.

Nl. graslandgrond
Grond met een zeer humeuze bovengrond, die overgaat in
grijze minerale grond.

S. ängsjord
Jord med ett humusrikt ytskikt övergående i grå mineraljord.

O2

Eng. <u>Alpine Meadow soil</u>
Dark soil of meadows above timber line of mountains.

F. <u>Sol d'Humus Alpin</u>
Sol noir de prairie humide, au-dessus de la limite
de la forêt.

D. <u>alpiner Wiesenboden</u> (m)
Dunkler Wiesenboden oberhalb der Waldgrenze.

Esp. <u>suelo de prado alpino</u>
Suelo oscuro de prados húmedos por encima del límite
de la vegetación arbórea.

P. <u>solo dos Prados Alpestres</u>
Solo escuro de prados naturais, bastante húmidos,
situados acima do limite climático da floresta.

I. <u>terreno</u> (m) <u>umifero di alta montagna</u> (f)
Terreno scuro umido con vegetazione prativa al di
sopra del limite climatico del bosco.

Nl. <u>alpenweide grond</u>
Donker gekleurde grond van natte weide boven de
boomgrens.

S. <u>alpin ängsjord</u>
Mörk fuktig ängsjord ovanför trädgränsen.

Eng. (1) alluvial meadow soil
      (2) gleyed forest soil
          Ground-water soil derived from recent alluvial deposits;
          the water table in (1) is deeper than in (2).

F.   _____
          (1) Sol alluvial fluviatile de formation récente;
          (2) sol de même formation que (1) mais avec un plan
          d'eau plus près de la surface.

D.   (1) Auenboden (m)
      (2) Bruchwaldboden (m)
          Aus rezenter Flussablagerung entstandener Grundwasser-
          boden; Grundwasserspiegel bei (1) tiefer als bei (2).

Esp. _____
          Suelo hidropédico derivado de depósitos aluviales
          recientes; la capa freática en (1) es más profunda
          que en (2).

P.   (1) solo de prado aluvial
      (2) solo glei florestal
          Solo hidromórfico derivado de depósitos aluviais
          recentes; a toalha de água esta a um nível mais baixo
          em (1) do que em (2).

I.   (1) terreno (m) alluvionale prativo
      (2) terreno (m) a gley forestale
          Terreno trasportato dalle acque derivato da recenti
          depositi alluvionali; la falda freatica in (1) è più
          bassa che in (2).

Nl.   (1) alluviale weidegrond
      (2) vergleyde boschgrond
          Uit recente alluviale afzettingen ontstane grondwater
          bodem; de waterspiegel in (1) ligt dieper dan in (2).

S.   _____
          Grundvattenjordar bildade av recenta fluviala avlagrin-
          gar. Grundvattenståndet i (1) lägre än i (2).

Eng. **gley soil**
Soil with high ground water and iron-oxide accumulation in the region of the water table.

F. **sol à gley**
Sol présentant en profondeur une nappe phréatique au niveau de laquelle se produisent des phénomènes de réduction des oxydes de fer.

D. **Gleiboden (m)**
Boden mit hohem Grundwasserstand und Eisenoxydhydrat-Anreicherung (G-Horizont) im Bereich des Wasserspiegels.

Esp. **suelo gley**
Suelo caracterizado por una capa freática superficial y una zona de acumulación de óxido de hierro dentro de la región correspondiente a dicha capa.

P. **solo "glei"**
Solo com lençol freático elevado e que apresenta uma acumulação de óxido de ferro na região daquela toalha de água.

I. **terreno (m) a gley**
Terra con alta quantità d'acqua sotterranea; gli ossidi di ferro (orizzonte G) si accumulano nella falda freatica.

Nl. **gley grond**
Bodem met hoog grondwater en een opeenhoping van ijzer oxyde in de omgeving van de waterspiegel.

S. **gleijordmån**
Jordmåner bildade under inverkan av rel. högt grundvattenstånd. Karakteriseras av stråk och fläckar av utfällda järnoxider i grundvattennivån (den s.k. glei-horisonten).

Eng. Humic Gley soil
        Continually or intermittently moist soil with or with-
        out a peaty covering, but having a prominent dark A_1
        horizon and a gleyed horizon.

F. Sol Humifère à Gley
        Sol de prairies humides noir en surface, mais sans
        horizon supérieur tourbeux, présentant en profondeur
        un horizon réducteur.

D. Humus-Glei-Boden (m)
        Grundwasserboden nasser Wiesen, schwarz nahe der Ober-
        fläche, aber ohne Torfauflage.

Esp. suelo de glei húmico
        Suelo de prados húmedos, oscuro cerca de la superficie
        pero carente de una capa superior turbosa.

P. solo Glei húmico
        Solo dos prados mal drenados, não turfoso, mas escuro
        à superfície.

I. terreno (m) umico a glei
        Terreno dei prati umidi, scuro vicino alla superficie
        ma che non ha la parte superiore torbosa.

Nl. humeuze gleygrond
        Grond van natte weiden met een donker gekleurde, maar
        geenvenige bovengrond.

S. humusrik glcijord
        Jord på ängsmarker med högt grundvattenstånd, mork nära
        ytan men utan torvartat A-skikt.

ARID AND SEMI-ARID SOILS

SOLS ARIDES ET SEMI-ARIDES

SUELOS ARIDOS Y SEMIARIDOS

Eng. <u>Chernozem</u>
Dark, well drained grassland soil granular and rich
in humus to some depth, with or without concentration
of clay in the B horizon, and calcareous below.

F. <u>Chernozem</u>
Sol noire de steppe, grenu jusqu'à une certaine profondeur, saturé, non calcaire en surface, même sur
roche-mère calcaire.

D. <u>Tschernosem</u> (m)
<u>Schwarzerde</u> (f)
Dunkler humusreicher Steppenboden, krümelig bis zu
40 cm Tiefe und darunter, häufig auf Lössunterlage
(A-C-Profil).

Esp. <u>suelo chernozem</u>
Suelo oscuro de praderas, granular hasta una cierta
profundidad, subsuelo calcáreo.

P. <u>solo Chernozem</u>
Solo negro das estepes de estrutura granulosa até
ocrta profundidade e com ou sem acumulação de calcário.

I. <u>cernosem</u> (m)
Terreno scuro con vegetazione erbacea, granulare
fino ad una certa profondità, e calcareo nella parte
sottostante.

Nl. <u>chernozem grond</u>
Donker gekleurde graslandgrond, tot enige diepte
korrelig en daaronder kalkhoudend.

S. <u>chernozemjord</u>
<u>svartjord</u>
Mörk, gräsbevuxen jord med kornig struktur till ett
visst djup och därunder kalkrik.

307

P2

Eng.   <u>Degraded Chernozem</u>
Dark well drained soil of grassland-forest transition,
with a grayish A_2 horizon.

F.   <u>Chernozem Dégradé</u>
Sol ayant les caractères des chernozems mais appauvri
en matière organique et en partie désaturé en surface,
plus ou moins lessivé.

D.   <u>degradierter Tschernosem</u> (m)
<u>degradierte Schwarzerde</u> (f)
Dunkler Boden mit etwas aufgehelltem gebleichten Horizont über einem braunen Horizont.

Esp.   <u>suelo chernozem degradado</u>
Suelo oscuro con un horizonte gris lixiviado que descansa sobre un horizonte pardo.

P.   <u>solo Chernozem Degradado</u>
Solo negro com um horizonte cinzento de eluviação
assente num horizonte pardo e que se forma na região
que separa os solos chernozem dos podzólicos onde a
floresta invadiu a estepe.

I.   <u>cernosem</u> (m) <u>degradato</u>
Terreno scuro con un orizzonte grigio lisciviato
sovrastante un orizzonte bruno.

Nl.   <u>gedegradeerde chernozem</u>
Donker gekleurde grond met een grijs gebleekte horizont liggende op een bruine horizont.

S.   <u>degraderad svartjord</u> (chernozem)
Mörk jord med ett grått urlakningsskikt över ett
brunt skikt.

Eng. Prairie soil
       (1) Soil developed under grass in humid temperate
       regions and resembling chernozem, but dark brown
       on the surface, ordinarily with some textural pro-
       file and without a prominent horizon of accumulated
       calcium carbonate.
       (2) A general term for all dark soils of treeless plains.

F.   Sol de la Prairie
       Sol de prairie de l'Amérique du Nord ressemblant à un
       chernozem, mais sans accumulation de carbonate de
       calcium.

D.   "Prärieboden" (m)
       Nordamerikanischer Graslandboden, der dem Tschernosem
       ähnelt aber keine Kalzium-Karbonat-Anreicherung h.t.

Esp. suelo de pradera
       Suelo de las zonas de pastos de Norte América,
       parecido al chernozem pero sin la acumulación de
       carbonato de calcio.

P.   solo de Pradaria
       Solo Norteamericano de pradaria semelhante no aspecto
       ao chernosem, porém sem acumulação de calcário.

I.   terreno (m) di prateria (f)
       Terreno a prato del Nord-America che assomiglia ai
       cernosem senza però presentare l'orizzonte di accu-
       mulo di carbonato di calcio.

Nl.   prairiegrond
       Noord-Amerikaanse graslandgrond, die op chernozem
       lijkt, maar zonder ophoping van calciumcarbonaat.

S.   präriejord
       Nordamerikansk gräsmarksjord likande svartjord men
       utan anrikning av kalciumkarbonat.

P4

Eng. <u>black earth</u>
    General term including chernozem and dark plastic
    clays of tropics.

F.   <u>terre noire</u>
    Terme général comprenant les chernozems et les
    argiles noires calcaires tropicales.

D.   <u>Schwarzerde</u> (f)
    Allgemeiner Ausdruck, der Tschernosem und dunkle
    kalkige Böden der Tropen einschliesst.

Esp. <u>suelo negro</u>
    Término general que incluye el chernozem y las
    arcillas oscuras calcáreas de los trópicos.

P.   <u>terra preta</u>
    Termo geral que inclui chernozem e argilas pretas
    tropicais.

I.   <u>terra</u> (f) <u>nera</u>
    Termine generico che comprende il cernosem e i
    terreni argillosi calcari scuri dei tropici.

Nl.   <u>zwarte aarde</u>
    Algemene term chernozem en donkere, kalkhoudende
    kleien van de tropen omvattend.

S.   <u>svartjord</u>
    Allmän term omfattande chernozem och mörka, kalkrika
    lerjordar i tropikerna.

Eng. black turf soil
        Dark clay soil usually with calcareous subsoil.

F. -----------------
        Argile noire, généralement avec sous-sol calcaire.

D. "schwarzer Rasenboden" (m)
        Dunkler toniger Boden, gewöhnlich mit kalkigem
        Untergrund.

Esp. suelo negro de "turf"
        Arcilla oscura generalmente con subsuelo calcáreo.

P. solo preto turfoso
        Solo negro, argiloso, assente usualmente em subsolo
        calcário.

I. ------------------
        Argilla scura generalmente con sottosuolo calcareo.

Nl. zwarte humeuze kleigrond
        Donkerbruine tot zwarte kleigrond, meestal met kalk-
        rijke ondergrond (Zuid-Afrika).

S. black-turf-jord
        Mörk lerjord vanligen med kalkrik alv.

Eng.   <u>High-veld Prairie soil</u>
      Brown sandy soil over heavier pea-iron layer over
      impermeable clay.

F.   -----------------------
      Sol sableux brun surmontant une couche plus lourde
      de pisolithes ferrugineux et une argile imperméable.

D.   "Hochlandprärieboden"
      Brauner sandiger Boden über schwerer Bohnerzschicht
      und undurchlässigem Tonuntergrund.

Esp.   <u>suelo de pradera de High Veld</u>
      Suelo pardo arenoso sobre una capa más pesada de
      nódulos de hierro sobre una arcilla impermeable.

P.   <u>solo de Pradaria do "high veld"</u>
      Solo arenoso pardo sobre uma camada mais compacta
      com concreções ferruginosas e sobre argila impermeável.

I.   <u>terreno (m) "high veld prairie"</u>
      Terreno sabbioso bruno, sopra uno strato più compatto
      con pisoliti ferruginose, soprastante a sua volta
      l'argilla impermeabile.

Nl.   <u>Hoogvlakte prairiegrond</u>
      Bruine zandgrond liggend op een zwaardere korrelige
      ijzerlaag op ondoorlatende klei (Zuid Afrika).

S.   <u>sydafrikansk präriejord</u>
      Jord med ett brunt sandigt jordskikt som överlagrar
      ett skikt med järnkonkreticner, under vilket ett
      ogenomssläppligt lerlager vidtar.

Eng. smonitza

     Hydromorphic black or dark gray soil of Yugoslavia,
     usually derived from calcareous clay overlying sand.
     The surface is leached of $CaCO_3$.

F.   "smonitza"

     Sol hydromorphique noir ou gris foncé de la Yougo-
     Slavie, généralement dérivé d'argile calcaire au-
     dessus de sable. Le calcaire est lessivé en surface.

D.   Smonitza

     Eine schwarzerderähnliche Bodenbildung anmooriger
     Herkunft, die als genetisches Glied einer Entwick-
     lungsreihe zur Braunerde (des humiden Gebiets)
     aufgefasst wird.

Esp. smonitza

     Suelo hidromórfico de color negro o gris oscuro casi
     siempre derivado de un material formado por una capa
     de arcilla calcarea sobre otra de arena. El carbonato
     de calcio ha sido lixiviado de la superficie. Este
     suelo se encuentra en Yugoeslavia.

P.   "smonitza"

     Solo hidromórfico preto ou cinzento escuro da Yugo-
     slávia, geralmente derivado duma argila calcária
     assente em areia. A camada superficial sofreu lava-
     gem do $CaCO_3$.

I.   "smonitza"

     Suolo idromorfico nero o grigio oscuro di Yugoslavia,
     generalmente derivato d'argilla calcarea sopra la
     sabbia. Lo strato superiore è liscivato da $CaCO_3$.

Nl.   smonitza

     Hydromorphische zwarte of donker grijze grond in
     Yugoslavië welke gewoonlijk ontstaan is op kalk-
     houdende klei liggend op zand. $CaCO_3$ is uit het
     oppervlak uitgeloogd.

S.   smonitza

     Chernozemliknande svart eller grå sumpjord från
     Jugoslavien, vanligen bildad av kalkhaltig ler över
     sand. Urlakning av $CaCO_3$ från ytskiktet.

Eng. <u>Chestnut soil</u>
Dark brown over lighter coloured soil overlying
a calcareous horizon.

F. <u>Sol Châtain</u>
Sol de steppe ou pseudo-steppe brun-foncé, au-
dessus d'un sous-sol de coloration plus claire;
non calcaire en surface même sur roch-mère
calcaire.

D. <u>kastanienfarbiger Boden</u> (m)
Steppenboden mit dunkelbraunem — im Vergleich
zum Tschernosem humusärmerem — A Horizont über
hellerem Untergrund (A-C-Profil).

Esp. <u>suelo castaño</u>
Suelo pardo oscuro sobre un subsuelo de colorido
más claro situada a su vez encima de un horizonte
calcáreo.

P. <u>solo Castanho</u>
Solo com horizonte superficial pardo escuro que
gradualmente passa a um mais claro e por fim a
uma camada calcária.

I. <u>terra</u> (f) <u>castana</u>
Terreno bruno scuro sovrastante uno strato di
colore più tenue che a sua volta ricopre un
orizzonte calcareo.

Nl. <u>kastanjebruine grond</u>
Donkerbruine grond met lichter gekleurde ondergrond rustend op een horizont met kalk-accumulatie.

S. <u>kastanjebrun jord</u>
Jord med överst ett mörkbrunt ytskikt, under vilket
finnes ett ljusare skikt, som överlagrar ett kalkrikt skikt.

Eng. <u>Brown (steppe) soil</u>
        Brown to light brown nearly neutral soil usually
        overlying a calcareous horizon.

F. <u>Sol Brun Subaride</u>
        Sol de steppe ou pseudo-steppe brun en surface;
        peu ou pas calcaire en surface même sur roche
        mère calcaire.

D. <u>"brauner Boden"</u>
        Über einem kalkreichen Horizont ausgebildeter brauner
        bis hellbrauner Boden der Halbwüste innerhalb der ost-
        europäischen Entwicklungsreihe: Wüste — grauer Boden
        — brauner Boden — kastanienfarbiger Boden — Tscher-
        nosem.

Esp. <u>suelo pardo</u>
        Suelo pardo que varía a un pardo más claro, que des-
        cansa sobre un horizonte calcáreo.

P. <u>solo Pardo</u>
        Solo com horizonte superficial pardo que imerge
        gradualmente num mais claro e por fim num horizonte
        calcário.

I. <u>terra</u> (f) <u>bruna</u>
        Terreno bruno che passa gradatamente a un orizzonte
        marrone chiaro sovrastante un orizzonte calcareo.

Nl. <u>Bruine grond</u>
        Bruine tot lichtbruine grond op een kalkrijke horizont.

S. <u>brun halvökenjord</u>
        Brun till ljusbrun jord met ett undre kalkrikt skikt.

Eng. <u>Reddish Brown (steppe)soil</u>
   Reddish brown soil grading into heavier soil overlying a calcareous horizon.

F. <u>Sol Brun-rouge</u>
   Sol brun ou brun-rougeâtre en surface, plus rouge
   et souvent plus argileux en profondeur et à teneur
   en matière organique décroissante; sur roche mère
   calcaire, il est en partie décalcifié en surface et
   comporte un encroutement en profondeur.

D. <u>"rötlich-brauner Boden"</u> (m), (<u>Halbwüstenboden</u>)
   Rötlich-brauner Boden, der mit der Tiefe schwerer
   wird und im Untergrund einen Kalkhorizont hat.

Esp. <u>suelo pardo rojizo</u>
   Suelo pardo rojizo que pasa progresivamente a un
   suelo más pesado que yace sobre un horizonte calcáreo.

P. <u>solo Pardo-avermelhado</u>
   Solo com horizonte superficial pardo-avermelhado,
   passando gradualmente para um material mais argiloso
   pardo-avermelhado escuro ou vermelho, e depois para
   um horizonte de acumulação de calcário.

I. <u>terra</u> (f) <u>rossa bruna</u>
   Terreno bruno rossastro che passa gradualmente ad
   un orizzonte compatto sovrastante un orizzonte
   calcareo.

Nl. <u>Roodbruine grond</u>
   Roodbruine grond overgaand in een zwaardere ondergrond liggende op een kalkrijke horizont.

S. <u>rödbrun jord</u>
   Rödbrun jord med ett kalkrikt skikt.

Eng. <u>Noncalcic Brown soil</u>
Brown to reddish weakly leached soil with slightly
acid light brown A horizon over darker B horizon.

F. <u>Sol Brun subaride (non calcaire)</u>
(Non différencié en français du sol brun subaride
sur calcaire.)

D. <u>"kalkfreier brauner Boden"</u> (m)
Rötlicher Boden mit schwach saurem hellbraunem
A-Horizont über dunklerem B-Horizont.

Esp. <u>suelo pardo no cálcico</u>
Suelo rojizo con un horizonte A pardo claro ligeramente ácido sobre un horizonte B más oscuro.

P. <u>solo Pardo sem Calcário</u>
Solo avermelhado com horizonte A pardo avermelhado
claro, ligeiramente ácido, sobre um horizonte B
mais escuro.

I. <u>terra</u> (f) <u>bruna a calcarea</u>
Terreno leggermente lisciviato da brunoa rossastro
con orizzonte A bruno chiaro leggermente acido
sopra un orizzonte B più scuro.

Nl. <u>kalkarme Bruine subariede grond</u>
Roodachtige bruine, weinig uitgeloogde grond met
een zwak zure licht-bruine A-horizont op een donk-
erder B-horizont.

S. <u>kalkfattig brunjord</u>
Rödaktig jord med ett svagt surt ljusbrunt A-skikt
över ett mörkare B-skikt.

Eng.   <u>Reddish Chestnut soil</u>
> Dark reddish brown soil grading into heavier soil
> overlying a calcareous horizon.

F.   <u>Sol Châtain-rouge</u>
> Sol peu rouge en surface, plus rouge et souvent plus
> argileux en profondeur à teneur en matière   unique
> élevée en surface et progressivement décroi nte en
> profondeur; sur roche mère calcai ., il est décalcifié
> en surface et comporte un encroutement ou des concré-
> tions calcaires en profondeur.

D.   <u>"rötlich-kastanienfarbiger Boden"</u> (m)
> Oben rötlicher, nach unten stärker rot und tonig
> werdender Boden, auf kalkigem Muttergestein.

Esp.   <u>suelo castaño rojizo</u>
> Suelo pardo rojizo que pasa progresivamente a un sub-
> suelo más pesado que yace sobre un horizonte calcáreo.

P.   <u>solo Castanho-avermelhado</u>
> Solo com uma superfície parda escura de tons rosados
> ou avermelhados, seguida de camada mais argilosa pardo-
> avermelhada, assente numa acumulação de calcário.

I.   <u>terra</u> (f) <u>castana rossastra</u>
> Terreno bruno rossastro che passa gradualmente ad un
> orizzonte più compatto sovrastante un orizzonte cal-
> careo.

Nl.   <u>Roodachtige kastanjebruine grond</u>
> Roodbruine grond overgaande in een zwaardere grond
> liggende op een kalkrijke horizont.

S.   <u>rödaktig kastanjebrun jord</u>
> Jord med rödbrunt ytskikt på styv alv över ett kalk-
> rikt skikt.

Eng. Reddish Prairie soil
        Reddish brown somewhat acid soil with **rather clayey**
        subsoil.

F.   Sol Rouge de la Prairie
        Sol faiblement à moyennement acide en surface,
        passant progressivement à un sous-sol plus lourd
        au-dessus de la roche-mère. (Non utilisé en
        français.)

D.   "rötlicher Prärieboden" (m)
        Rötlich-brauner schwach saurer Boden mit ziemlich
        schwerem Untergrund.

Esp. suelo rojizo de pradera
        Suelo pardo-rojizo, algo ácido, con subsuelo más
        bien pesado.

P.   solo Avermelhado de Pradaria
        Solo pardo-avermelhado escuro, fraca ou mediana-
        mente ácido, que gradualmente, através dum material
        avermelhado um tanto mais argiloso, atinge o mater-
        ial originário.

I.   terra (f) rossastra di prateria
        Terreno alquanto acido bruno rossiccio con sotto-
        suolo piuttosto compatto.

Nl.   Roodachtige prairiegrond
        Roodachtige, iets zure grond met een **tamelijk**
        zware ondergrond.

S.   rödfärgad präriejord
        Rödaktigt brun något sur jord med en ganska **styv**
        alv.

P14

Eng. <u>sierozem</u>
<u>Gray Desert soil</u>
Brownish gray soil overlying a calcareous horizon
or lime pan.

F. <u>sol gris subdésertique</u>
Sol gris en surface, plus clair en-dessous et
différencié de sa roche mère par un faible entraînement par l'eau des éléments solubles ou par des phénomènes d'évaporation en surface.

D. <u>"Sierozem"</u> (m)
Bräunlich-grauer Boden über einer Kalkschicht.

Esp. <u>suelo sierozem</u>
Suelo gris parduzco que descansa sobre un horizonte
calcáreo o una capa calcárea.

P. <u>"sierozem"</u>
Solo com um horizonte superficial cinzento-pardacento,
imergindo, através de material mais claro, numa camada
de acumulação de carbonatos e, frequentemente, numa
surraipa.

I. <u>sierozem</u> (m)
Terreno grigio castagno sovrastante un orizzonte o uno
strato calcareo.

Nl. <u>sierozem</u>
Bruingrijze grond liggende op een kalkrijke horizont
of een kalklaag.

S. <u>sierozem</u>
Brungrå jord med ett kalkrikt ofta hårdnat skikt.

320

Eng. Desert soil
> Soil of arid regions, low in organic matter, usually
> having calcareous subsoil or lime pan.

F. sol des déserts
sol subdésertique
> Sol des régions arides, pauvre en matière organique,
> comportant souvent près da la surface une croute cal-
> caire ou faiblement saline.

D. Wüstenboden (m)
> Boden arider Gebiete, mit geringem Humusgehalt und
> meist mit kalkhaltigem Untergrund oder Kalksohle.

Esp. suelo desértico
> Suelo de regiones áridas, pobre en materia orgánica,
> que tiene un subsuelo calcáreo o una capa calcárea.

P. solo Desértico
> Solo das regiões áridas, pobre em matéria orgânica,
> usualmente assente num material calcário e, com fre-
> quência, em crostas calcárias.

I. terreno (m) desertico
> Terreni, delle regioni aride, con scarsa sostanza
> organica, che ha un sottosuolo calcareo o un cros-
> tone calcareo.

Nl. woestijngrond
> Grond van ariede streken met weinig organische stof
> en met een kalkhoudende ondergrond of een kalkbank
> in het profiel.

S. ökenjord
> Jord i arida områden, fattig på organisk substans
> och med en kalkrik alv, som stundom har kalk-
> konkretioner.

P16

Eng. <u>Red Desert soil</u>
Pinkish gray to light reddish brown soil over a some-
what more clayey, yellowish red or red subsoil in
desert or semi-desert regions.

F. <u>Sol Rouge Désertique</u>
Sol des régions désertiques ou sub-désertiques gris-
rosé ou brun rouge clair reposant sur un sous-sol
légèrement plus argileux rouge jaunâtre ou rouge.
(Non utilisé en français - utilisé aux Etats-Unis.)

D. <u>roter Wüstenboden</u> (m)
Rosa-grau bis rötlich brauner Boden über tonigerem,
gelblich-rotem oder rotem Untergrund in Wüsten- oder
Halbwüstengegenden.

Esp. <u>suelo rojo desértico</u>
En regiones desérticas o semidesérticas, suelo de
color gris-rojizo a marron-rojizo sobre un subsuelo
un poco más arcilloso, amarillo-rojizo o rojo.

P. <u>solo Vermelho Desértico</u>
Solo de côr cinzento-rosada a pardo-avermelhada clara
sobre subsolo vermelho-amarelado ou vermelho, que
aparece nas regiões desérticas ou semi-desérticas.

I. <u>terreno</u> (m) <u>rosso desertico</u>
Terreno da grigio-rosa a leggermente rosso-marrone
sopra a un sottosuolo maggiormente argilloso, rosso-
giallastro, in regioni desertiche o semidesertiche.

Nl. <u>Rode woestijngrond</u>
Zalmkleurig grijze tot licht rood-bruine grond met een
iets zwaardere, geelrode of rode ondergrond, voorkomend
in woestijn- of half-woestijngebieden.

S. <u>röd ökenjord</u>
Svagt rödgrå till ljust rödbrun jord över en något
lerrikare gulröd eller röd alv i öken- eller halv-
ökenområden.

Section Q

SALINE AND ALKALI SOILS

SOLS SALINS ET ALCALINS

SUELOS SALINOS Y ALCALINOS

Eng. **saline soil**
      halomorphic soil
      Soil whose properties have been determined by the
      presence of salts.

F.   **sol salé**
      sol halomorphe
      Sol dont les propriétés résultent de la présence
      de sels.

D.   **Salzboden (m)**
      halomorpher Boden (m)
      Boden, dessen Eigenschaften durch die Gegenwart von
      Salz bestimmt sind.

Esp. **suelo salino**
      suelo halomórfico
      Suelo cuyas propiedades han sido determinadas por
      la presencia de sales.

P.   **solo salino**
      solo salgado
      solo halomorfico
      sapal
      Solo cuja principal caracteristica resulta da acumu-
      lação de sals alcalinos.

I.   **terreno (m) salato**
      terreno (m) alomorfo
      Terreno le cui proprietà sono state determinate dalla
      presenza di sali.

Nl.   **zoute grond**
      Grond waarvan de eigenschappen worden bepaald door de
      aanwezigheid van zouten.

S.   **saltjord**
      halomorf jord
      Jord vars egenskaper äro bestämda av närvaro av salter.

Q2

Eng. <u>Solonchak</u>
        Saline soil without structure.

F.   <u>sol salin</u>
    <u>Solonchak</u>
        Sol salé dont la structure n'est pas dégradée.

D.   <u>Solontschak</u> (m)
        Strukturloser Salzboden mit typischen Salzanhäufungen
        an der Oberfläche.

Esp. <u>"solonchak"</u>
        Suelo salino sin estructura.

P.   <u>Solonchak</u>
        Solo salino, em regra de côr clara, sem diferenciação
        estrutural característica.

I.   <u>solonchak</u> (m)
        Terreno salso senza struttura.

Nl.   <u>solonchak</u>
        Zoute grond zonder structuur.

S.   <u>solonchak</u>
    <u>saltjord</u>
        Saltjord utan struktur.

Eng.　Solonetz
　　　　Formerly saline soil from which the salts have been
　　　　leached, with cloddy prismatic or columnar B horizon.

F.　　Solonetz
　　　　Sol salé lessivé avec un horizon B prismatique ou en
　　　　colonne.

D.　　Solonetz
　　　　Schwach ausgelaugter Salzsodaboden von scholliger,
　　　　prismatischer oder säuliger Struktur.

Esp.　"solonetz"
　　　　Suelo salino ligeramente lixiviado con horizonte B
　　　　terronoso, prismático o columnar.

P.　　Solonetz
　　　　Solo salino com um horizonte superficial variável, de
　　　　solo freável, assente num horizonte duro, escuro, em
　　　　geral com estrutura colunar ou prismática, apresentam
　　　　em regra elevada alcalinidade.

I.　　solonetz (m)
　　　　Terreno salso leggermente lisciviato con l'orizzonte
　　　　B zolloso, prismatico o coloniforme.

Nl.　　solonetz
　　　　Zwak uitgeloogde zoute grond met kluiterige, prismatische
　　　　of kolomvormige B-horizont.

S.　　solonetz
　　　　Obetydligt urlakad saltjord med prismatisk eller pelar-
　　　　struktur i torrt tillstånd.

Q4

Eng. <u>Solod, (Soloth)</u>
     Leached saline soil (degraded solonetz) having a pale A_2 horizon and a degraded fine-textured B horizon.

F.   "<u>Solod</u>"
     Sol salin lessivé ayant un horizon A_2 pâle et quelquefois lourd.

D.   <u>Soloti</u>
     Degradierter ausgelaugter Alkaliboden mit fahlem A_2- und verdichtetem B-Horizont.

Esp. "<u>solodi</u>"
     Suelo salino lixiviado que tiene un horizonte A_2 de color más claro, a veces pesado.

P.   "<u>Solod</u>"
     Solo salino com uma camada superficial delgada de solo pardo, freável assente num horizonte cinzento, lavado, seguido por um horizonte pardo ou pardo escuro.

I.   <u>soloti</u> (m)
     Terreno salso lisciviato che ha un orizzonte A_2 chiaro e talvolta compatto e un orizzonte B a intessitura fine degradato.

Nl.   <u>solod</u>
     Uitgeloogde zoutgrond, die een licht gekleurde en soms zware A_2-horizont heeft.

S.   <u>degraderad alkalijord</u>
    <u>solod (solot)</u>
     Urlakad saltjord med ett ljust stundom mäktigt A_2-skikt.

Eng. <u>szik soil</u>
>   Saline or alkaline soil of Hungary.

F. <u>sol "szik"</u>
>   Sol à alcalis de Hongrie.

D. <u>Szik-Boden</u> (m)
>   Alkaliboden der ungarischen Tiefebene.

Esp. <u>suelo "szik"</u>
>   Suelo alcalino de Hungría.

P. <u>solo "szik"</u>
>   Solo alcalino da Hungria.

I. ------------
>   Terreno alcalino dell'Ungheria.

Nl. <u>szik grond</u>
>   Alkali grond van Hongarije.

S. <u>ungersk saltjord</u>
   <u>szikjord</u>
>   Alkalijord i Ungern.

Q6

Eng. <u>mallee soil</u>
Light brown, slightly leached saline soil of semi-desert
regions of southern Australia, whose characteristics are
determined by wind-blown oceanic salt.

F. ----------
Sol salin brun clair de la zone semi-désertique
d'Australie du Sud, peu lessivé et caractérisé par les
sels océaniques transportés par le vant.

D. <u>Mallee-boden</u> (m)
Hellbrauner, schwach ausgelaugter Salzboden der Wüsten-
steppen Südaustraliens, gekennzeichnet durch windge-
triebenes Meersalz.

Esp. ----------
Suelo salino ligeramente lixiviado, castaño claro, de
las regiones semi-desérticas de Australia meridional
cuyas características están determinadas por sales
oceánicas acarreadas por el viento.

P. <u>solo "malee"</u>
Solo salino de côr parda clara, ligeiramente lavado, que
aparece nas regiões semideserticas do sul da Austrália,
cujas características são determinadas pelos sais trazi-
dos do mar por acção do vento.

I. ----------
Terreno salino bruno chiaro della zona semi-desertica
dell'Australia del Sud, poco lisciviato e caratteriz-
zato per sali oceanici portati dal vento.

Nl. ----------
Licht-bruine weinig uitgeloogde zoute grond in de half-
woestijn gebieden van zuid Australië, welker eigenschappen zijn gekenmerkt door op de wind gedragen zout van de
oceaan.

S. ----------
Ljusbrun, svagt urlakad saltjordmån i de arida områdena
i södra Australien. Dess egenskaper bestämmes till stor
del av vindburna havssalter.

330

Section R

TROPICAL AND SUB-TROPICAL SOILS

SOLS TROPICAUX ET SUB-TROPICAUX

SUELOS TROPICALES ET SUBTROPICALES

Eng.   laterite soil
       Latosol
             Soil with thin A_O and A_1 layers over reddish or red
             deeply weathered material which is low in silica and
             high in sesquioxides.

F.   Sol Latéritique
             Sol ayant des horizons A_O et A_1 peu épais au-dessus d'un
             matériau profondément altéré rougeâtre appauvri en silice
             et enrichi en hydroxydes de fer et d'alumine.

D.   Lateritboden (m)
             Boden mit dünnen A_O- und A_1-Schichten über rötlichem
             oder rotem tief verwittertem Material das wenig Kiesel-
             säure und viel Sesquioxyde enthält.

Esp.   suelo laterítico
             Suelo con capas A_O y A_1 delgadas sobre un material rojizo
             o rojo, profundamente meteorizado.

P.   latosolo
             Solo com A_O e A_1 delgados assentes em material vermelho
             ou avermelhado muito meteorizado que contém muitos ses-
             quióxidos e pouca sílica.

I.   terreno (m) lateritico
             Terreno in cui gli strati sottili A_O e A_1 si trovano
             sopra del materiale profondamente trasformato rossastro
             o rosso che è povero di silice e con alto contenuto in
             sesquiossidi.

Nl.   laterietgrond
             Grond met dunne A_O- en A_1-horizonten op roodachtige of
             rode, diep verweerd materiaal met een laag gehalte aan
             silicaten en een hoog percentage sesquioxyden.

S.   lateritjord
             Jord met tunt A_O- och A_1-skikt över ett rödaktigt eller
             rött starkt förvittrat material.

R2

Eng.   Reddish Brown Lateritic soil
      Predominantly red friable clay soil passing into reti-
      culately mottled red and white clay.

F.   Sol Rouge Latéritique
      Sol riche en hydroxydes de fer et aluminium généralement
      très profond, peu rouge en surface, plus rouge en dessous,
      assez friable même lorsqu'il est de texture argileuse,
      comportant en profondeur une argile tachetée au-dessus
      d'une roche mère fortement décomposée.

D.   "rötlich-brauner lateritischer Boden" (m)
      Vorwiegend roter sesquioxydreicher krümeliger Tropen-
      boden mit Übergang zu netzartig geflecktem rotem und
      weissem Ton.

Esp.   suelo laterítico pardo rojizo
      Suelo predominantemente de arcilla roja, friable, pasando
      a una arcilla de veteado reticular roja y blanco.

P.   solo Pardo-avermelhado Laterítico
      Solo com a superfície granulosa pardo-avermelhada escura,
      horizonte B de argila vermelha freável e material origi-
      nário de argila recticularmente manchada de vermelho e
      branco.

I.   terra (f) lateritica bruna rossastra
      Terreno argilloso friabile prevalentemente rosso che
      passa ad una argilla reticolata screziata di rosso e di
      bianco.

Nl.   Roodbruine lateritische grond
      Overwegend rode, kruimelige kleigrond overgaand in net-
      vormig gevlekte rode en witte klei.

S.   rödbrun lateritisk jord
      Företrädesvis röd lös lerjord övergående i marmorerad
      röd och vit lera.

Eng. yellowish brown lateritic soil
> Yellowish brown friable clay soil grading into yellow
> or reddish yellow clay.

F. sol beige latéritique
> Sol riche en hydroxydes de fer et d'alumine généralement
> très profond, gris-beige en surface, puis plus beige au
> dessous, assez friable, même lorsqu'il est de texture
> argileuse, comportant en profondeur une argile tachetée
> au dessus d'une roche mère fortement décomposée.

D. "gelblich-brauner lateritischer Boden" (m)
> Gelblich-brauner sesquioxydreicher Tropenboden, krümelig
> mit Übergang zu gelbem oder rötlich-gelbem Ton im Unter-
> grund.

Esp. suelo laterítico pardo amarillento
> Suelo arcilloso pardo amarillento, friable variando
> gradualmente hacia una arcilla amarilla o amarilla rojiza.

P. solo pardo-amarelado laterítico
> Solo argiloso, freável, pardo-amarelado, passando gradual-
> mente a argilas amarelas ou amarelo-avermelhadas, que
> cobrem materiais originários não muito manchados.

I. terra (f) lateritica bruna giallognola
> Terreno argilloso friabile bruno giallognolo che via via
> passa ad una argilla gialla o giallo rossastra.

Nl. geelbruine lateritische grond
> Geelbruine brokkelige kleigrond overgaande in gele of
> roodachtig gele klei.

S. lateritisk gulbrun jord
> Gulbrun lös lerjord övergående i gul eller rödgul lera.

R4

Eng. <u>ground-water laterite</u>
Soil with high water table and a coarsely mottled ferruginous subsoil which either is hard or will harden on exposure.

F. <u>latérite de nappe</u>
Sol tropical à sous-sol compact tacheté, de teinte rouge, déjà durci (cuirasse) ou capable de durcir.

D. <u>"Grundwasserlaterit" (m)</u>
Tropischer Boden mit hohem Grundwasserstand und rotem eisenschmüssigem Untergrund, der hart ist oder beim Zutagetreŧen hart wird.

Esp. <u>laterita hidromórfica</u>
Suelo tropical que tiene un subsuelo rojo y blanco que puede endurecerse en contacto con el aire.

P. <u>laterite hidromórfica</u>
Solo tropical, com horizonte A esbranquiçado com concreções e surraipas celulares de compostos de ferro e alumínio e com uma toalha de água alternadamente alta e baixa.

I. <u>crosta (f) lateritica dovuta ad acqua sotterranea</u>
Terreno tropicale che ha sottosuolo rosso e bianco che può indurire quando esposti all'aria.

N1. <u>grondwater-lateriet</u>
Tropische grond met een rode en witte ondergrond, die hard kan worden als hij aan licht en lucht wordt blootgesteld.

S. <u>grundvattenlaterit</u>
Tropisk jordmån med högt grundvattenstånd.

Eng. <u>Nonlaterized Red earth</u>
   Well drained, moderately leached, olod structured, tropical soil free from calcium carbonate.

F. <u>Sol Rouge non Latéritisé</u>
   Sol tropical bien drainé, moyennement lessivé, à structure motteuse et exempte de carbonate de calcium, non
   appauvri en silice.

D. <u>nichtlaterisierter Rotlehm</u> (m)
   Gut dränierter mässig ausgelaugter, tropischer Boden,
   frei von Kalziumkarbonat.

Esp. <u>tierra roja no laterizada</u>
   Suelo tropical bien drenado, moderadamente lixiviado,
   de estructura terronosa, libre de carbonato de calcio.

P. <u>terra Vermelha não Laterítica</u>
   Solo tropical, sem calcário, bem drenado, moderadamente
   lavado e de estrutura em torrões.

I. <u>terra</u> (f) <u>rossa non laterizzata</u>
   Terreno tropicale ben drenato, moderatamente lisciviato,
   a struttura zollosa, non contenente carbonato di calcio.

Nl. <u>niet-gelateriseerde roodaarde</u>
   Goed ontwaterde, tamelijk gebleekte tropische grond met
   een kluitstructuur en zonder calciumcarbonaat.

S. <u>icke-lateritiserad rödjord</u>
   Tropisk jord, som saknar kalciumkarbonat, är genomsläp-
   plig och måttligt urlakad.

Eng.   <u>Terra Rossa</u>
        Red base-saturated clayey soil formed from hard limestone
        in the Mediterranean climate.

F.   <u>Terra Rossa</u>
        Argile rouge saturée par les bases, formée par l'altéra-
        tion d'un calcaire.

D.   <u>Terra Rossa</u> (f)
        Auf Kalkstein gebildeter roter basengesättigter toniger
        Boden des Mittelmeergebietes.

Esp.   <u>Terra Rossa</u>
        Arcilla roja saturada de bases, proveniente de la altera-
        ción de la piedra caliza.

P.   <u>"Terra Rossa"</u>
        <u>solo Vermelho Mediterrânico</u> (calcário)
        <u>barrocal</u>
        Solo argiloso vermelho saturado de bases, proveniente de
        calcários.

I.   <u>terra</u> (f) <u>rossa</u>
        Terreno argilloso rosso saturo di basi formatesi da cal-
        cari.

Nl.   <u>Terra Rossa</u>
        Rode, met basen verzadigde klei, gevormd van kalksteen.

S.   <u>terra rossa</u>
        Röd basmättad lerjord bildad av kalksten.

Eng. red earth
>   Tropical soil usually leached, red, deep, clayey and
>   moderately low in combined silica. (Included with
>   latosol in U.S. usage.)

F.   Terre Rouge (latéritique)
>   Sol faiblement latéritique, sol des régions tropicales.

D.   Rotlehm (m)
>   Tropischer Boden, schwach laterisiert.

Esp. arcilla roja
>   Suelo tropical, generalmente lixiviado, rojo, profundo,
>   pesado y pobre en sílice.

P.   terra vermelha
>   Solo tropical geralmente lavado, vermelho, profundo,
>   argiloso e pobre cm sílica.

I.   terreno (m) rosso
>   Terreno tropicale (e subtropicale), generalmente lisci-
>   viato, rosso, (più o meno) profondo, (talora) pesante e
>   con esigue quantità di silice.

Nl.   rode lateritische grond
>   Rode, dikke, zware tropische kleigrond met een wezenlijk
>   doch laag gehalte aan kiezelzuur.

S.   rödjord
>   Tropisk jordmån vanligen urlakad, röd, djup ooh fattig
>   på kiselsyra.

R8

Eng. <u>red loam</u>
Tropical soil usually leached, red, deep, friable and
low in silica.

F. <u>limon rouge</u>
Roche ou sol friable riche en éléments fins, surtout
sable fin et limon, riche en oxyde de fer; calcaire
ou décalcifié et enrichi en argile.

D. <u>roter Lehm</u> (m)
Tropische Bodenart, meist ausgewaschen, durch Eisenoxyde
tief rot gefarbt und kieselsäurearm.

Esp. <u>tierra roja franca</u>
Suelo tropical, generalmente lixiviado, rojo, profundo,
friable y escaso de sílice.

P. <u>terra franca vermelha</u>
Solo tropical geralmente lavado, vermelho, profundo,
freável e pobre em sílica.

I. <u>terreno</u> (m) <u>argilloso rosso</u>
Terreno tropicale generalmente lisciviato, rosso, profondo, friabile e con esigue quantità di silice.

Nl. <u>rode leem</u>
Tropische grond, gewoonlijk uitgeloogd, dik, kruimelig
en met een laag gehalte aan kiezelzuur.

S. <u>röd lera</u>
Tropisk jordmån vanligen urlakad, röd, djup, lös och
fattig på kiselsyra.

Eng. <u>Gray Ferruginous soil</u>
Gray sandy soil overlying conspicuous iron concretions
overlying clay.

F. <u>Sol Ferrugineux Tropical Lessivé</u>
Sol sableux gris, surmontant un sous-sol riche en concré-
tions ferrugineuses nettement individualisées, lui-même
au dessus d'un horizon plus argileux.

D. "<u>grau-rostfarbiger Boden</u>" (m)
Grauer sandiger Boden über deutlichen Eisenkonkretionen
auf Tonunterlage.

Esp. <u>suelo gris ferruginoso</u>
Suelo arenoso gris yaciendo sobre concreciones de hierro
visibles que se encuentran sobre arcilla.

P. <u>solo Cinzento ferruginoso</u>
Solo arenoso cinzento sobre concreções ferruginosas distintas assentes, por sua vez, em argila.

I. <u>terreno</u> (m) <u>ferruginoso</u>
Terreno sabbioso grigio soprastanti un orizzonte ricco
di concrezioni ferruginose a sua volta ricoprente
l'argilla.

Nl. <u>Grijze roestige grond</u>
Grijze zandgrond met duidelijk zichtbare ijzerconcreties
liggend op klei.

S. <u>gråjord med järnutfällningar</u>
Jord med överst ett grått sandigt skikt över ett lager
med järnutfällningar under vilket ett lerlager vidtar.

Eng. <u>Gray tropical clay</u>
Calcareous or non-calcareous clay of tropical savannahs.

F. <u>argile grise tropicale</u>
Argile, de teinte foncée, calcaire, ou non, des savanes
tropicales.

D. <u>grauer Tropenton</u> (m)
Kalkhaltiger oder kalkfreier Senkenton tropischer Savan-
nen.

Esp. <u>arcilla gris tropical</u>
Arcilla calcárea o nó calcarea de sabanas tropicales.

P. <u>argila Cinzenta tropical</u>
Argila calcária ou não calcária das savanas tropicais.

I. <u>argilla</u> (f) <u>grigia tropicale</u>
Argilla calcarea o non calcarea delle savane tropicali.

Nl. <u>Grijze tropische kleigrond</u>
Kalkrijke of kalkarme kleigrond van tropische savanna's.

S. <u>grå tropisk lerjord</u>
Kalkrika eller kalkfattiga ler på tropiska grässlätter.

Eng. **regur**
      black cotton soil
            Dark coloured, usually calcareous tropical soil that
            swells when wet and cracks deeply on drying.

F.   **regur**
      sol noir à coton
            Sol tropical, collant quand il est humide et fissuré
            profondément quand il séche. Est souvent utilisé pour
            la culture du coton.

D.   **Regur** (m)
      "black cotton soil"
            Dunkler, schwerer tropischer Boden der bei Anfeuchtung
            schmiert und beim Austrocknen rissig ist.

Esp. **regur**
      suelo negro de algodón
            Suelo tropical que es pegajoso cuando mojado y que se
            agrieta profundamente al desecarse.

P.   **"regur"**
      solo preto do algodão
            Solo tropical de côr preta, pegajoso quando húmido e
            fendilhando profundamente quando seco.

I.   **regur**
      terra (f p) nera da cotone (m)
            Terreno tropicale che è attaccaticcio quando umido e
            che si fessura profondamente nell'essiccarsi.

Nl.   **regur**
      zwarte katoengrond
            Donkergekleurde tropische grond, die kleverig is onder
            vochtige omstandigheden en diep scheurt bij indrogen.

S.   **regur**
      svart bomullsjord
      tropisk svartjord
            Tropisk jordmån med mörk basrik A-horisont och med kalk-
            anrikningsskikt på visst djup.

Eng. <u>tirs</u>
Black clay soil of North Africa, resembling regur.

F. <u>tirs</u>
Sol noir fortement argileux, à structure très compacte
dont la matière organique évolue au moins partiellement
en anaérobiose. Fréquent au Maroc.

D. <u>Tirs</u>
Schwarzer Boden in Nord-Afrika der in seinen Eigenschaften dem Regur ähnlich ist.

Esp. <u>tirs</u>
Suelo arcilloso de color negro, existente en Africa del
Norte, semejante al regur.

P. "tirs"
Solo negro do Norté de África, semelhante ao "regur".

I. <u>tirs</u>
Terreno nero del Nord Africa, che rassomiglia al regur.

Nl. <u>tirs</u>
Zwarte grond van Noord-Afrika die op regur lijkt.

S. <u>tirs</u>
Nordafrikansk svartjord, liknande regur.

Section S

INTRAZONAL AND AZONAL SOILS

SOLS INTRAZONAUX ET AZONAUX

SUELOS INTRAZONALES Y AZONALES

Eng. Rendzina
humus-carbonate soil
Dark calcareous, usually shallow soil formed on soft
limestone.

F. rendzine
Sol calcaire riche en matière organique formé sur calcaire.

D. Rendzina (f)
Humuskarbonatboden (m)
Auf Kalkstein gebildeter dunkler humusreicher Boden im
humiden Bereich der gemässigten Klimas; ähnlich der
Schwarzerde, jedoch höhere Durchlässigkeit, geringere
Tiefgründigkeit.

Esp. suelo rendzina
Suelo calcáreo oscuro formado sobre piedra caliza.

P. Rendzina
Solo com horisonte superficial freável pardo ou negro
seguido por material calcário cinzento claro ou avermelhado.

I. rendzina (m)
Terreno calcareo scuro formatosi su rocce calcaree.

Nl. rendzina
Donkere, kalkhoudende grond, gevormd op kalksteen.

S. rendzina
Mörk kalkrik jord bildad på kalkstens grund.

347

Eng. <u>mountain soil</u>
  Soil, usually skeletal, formed in mountain regions mainly
  by physical weathering.

F. <u>sol de montagnes</u>
  Sol généralement squelettique, formé surtout par désagré-
  gation méchanique (des roches) dans les régions montag-
  neuses.

D. <u>Gebirgsboden</u> (m)
  Boden, gewöhnlich Skelettboden, in Gebirgsgegenden, haupt-
  sächlich durch physikalische Verwitterung gebildet.

Esp. <u>suelo de montaña</u>
  Suelo generalmente esquelético formado principalmente por
  meteorización física en regiones montañosas frías.

P. <u>solo de montanha</u>
  Solo geralmente esquelético, formado em regiões montan-
  hosas frias principalmente por meteorização física.

I. <u>terreno</u> (m) <u>di montagna</u> (f)
  Terreno generalmente scheletrico, formatosi in regioni
  montane fresche, prevalentemente per disgregazione.

Nl. <u>gebergte grond</u>
  Grond, gewoonlijk een lithosol, in koele bergachtige
  streken gevormd, hoofdzakelijk door physische verwering.

S. <u>alpin jord</u>
  Jord i bergstrakter huvudsakligen bildad genom fysikalisk vittring.

Eng. <u>skeletal soil</u> (U.K.)
        Soil consisting of nearly unweathered rock fragments.
      <u>Lithosol</u> (U.S.)
        Thin, stony soil shallow over bedrock without a defi-
        nite B horizon, due to relative youth.

F.   <u>sol squelettique</u>
        Sol formé de fragments de roches très peu altérés.

D.   <u>Skelettboden</u> (m)
     <u>Gesteinsboden</u> (m)
        Boden, der fast nur aus unverwitterten Gesteinstrümmern
        besteht.

Esp. <u>suelo esquelético</u>
        Suelo formado por fragmentos de rocas casi inalteradas.

P.   <u>solo esqueletico</u>
        Solo constituido quase exclusivamente por fragmentos
        rochosos.

I.   <u>terreno</u> (m) <u>sassoso</u> (pietroso)
        Terreno che è formato (in prevalenza) da frammenti di
        roccia poco alterati dai vari agenti.

Nl. <u>lithosol</u>
        Grond bestaande uit onverweerde of bijna niet verweerde
        gesteentefragmenten.

S.   <u>skelettjord</u>
        Jord som till större delen består av kemiskt ovittrade
        bergartsfragment.

S4

Eng. <u>secondary soil</u>
<u>transported soil</u>
Soil formed on transported material.

F. <u>sol de seconde formation</u>
Sol formé sur des matériaux transportés.

D. <u>allochthoner Boden</u> (m)
<u>umgelagerter Boden</u> (m)
Boden, der vom Ausgangsgestein entfernt worden ist,
sich daher an sekundärer Lagerstätte befindet.

Esp. <u>suelo secundario</u>
Suelo formado sobre material transportado.

P. <u>solo secundário</u>
Solo formado a partir de material transportado.

I. <u>terreno</u> (m) <u>secondario</u>
Terreno formato da materiale di trasporto.

Nl. <u>secundaire grond</u>
<u>allochtone grond</u>
Grond gevormd op verplaatst materiaal.

S. <u>allokton jord</u>
Jord bildad av transporterat material.

Eng. <u>residual soil</u>
     Soil resting on the material from which it was formed.

F. <u>sol résiduel</u>
     Sol subsistant sur les matières à partir desquelles il
     a été formé.

D. <u>Ortsboden</u> (m)
    <u>autochthoner Boden</u> (m)
     Boden, der dem Ausgangsmaterial aufliegt, aus dem er
     gebildet wurde.

Esp. <u>suelo residual</u>
     Suelo que descansa sobre el material del cual fué formado.

P. <u>solo residual</u>
     Solo assente em material a partir do qual se formou.

I. <u>terreno</u> (m) <u>residuale</u>
     Terreno che rimane sul materiale dal quale è stato origi-
     nato.

Nl. <u>autochtone grond</u>
     Grond rustend op het materiaal, waaruit hij gevormd werd.

S. <u>sedentär jord</u>
     Jord som vilar på sitt ursprungsmaterial.

Eng. <u>transitional soil</u>
   Soil intermediate in character between two different
   soils.

F. <u>sol de transition</u>
   Sol intermédiaire entre deux types de sol différents.

D. <u>Übergangsboden</u> (m)
   Boden, der charakteristische Merkmale zweier ver-
   schiedener Bodentypen aufweist.

Esp. <u>suelo de transición</u>
   Suelo que participa de los caracteres de dos grupos
   de suelos diferentes.

P. <u>solo de transição</u>
   Solo contendo características intermediárias as de
   dois solos diferentes.

I. <u>terreno</u> (m) <u>di transizione</u> (f)
   Terreno che rassomiglia in certo modo a due tipi
   diversi di terreno.

Nl. <u>overgangsgrond</u>
   Grond, die lijkt op twee andere gronden.

S. <u>övergångsjord</u>
   Jord vars egenskaper ansluta sig till två andra jord-
   typers.

Eng. ------------
    Structureless soil of high silt content that gets muddy
    when wetted.

F.   terre battante
    Sol sans structure et riche en limon, qui devient facile-
    ment bourbeux par humectation. Se flaçant en surface.

D.   Flottlehm (m)
   Fliesserde (f)
    Strukturloser Boden mit hohem Schluffanteil, der bei
    Befeuchtung leicht zerfliesst.

Esp. ------------
    Suelo carente de estructura, rico en limo que se vuelve
    pantanoso al mojarse.

P.   solo limoso
   nateiro
    Solo sem estrutura e com elevada quantidade de limo, que
    se torna lamacento quando humedecido.

I.   ------------
    Terreno senza struttura e riccho di limo, che diviene
    facilmente melmoso quando bagnato.

Nl. ------------
    Structuurloze bodem met een hoog sloefgehalte die bij
    bevochtiging modderig wordt.

S.   flytjord
    Jordar i enkelstruktur med hög mjälahalt. Blir lätt
    flytande vid hög vattenhalt.

Eng. -----------
Soil formed on basic eruptive rock.

F. -----------
Sol développé sur des roches éruptives basiques.

D. Erubas-Boden
Auf basischem Eruptivgestein gebildeter Boden.

Esp. -----------
Suelo formado en roca eruptiva básica.

P. -----------
Solo formado a partir de rochas eruptivas básicas.

I. -----------
Terreno sviluppato su rocce eruttive alcaline.

Nl. erubas grond
Een op een basisch eruptief gesteente gevormde grond.

S. -----------
Jord bildad in situ av basiska eruptiva bergarter.

Eng. ------------
    Sandy soil that has been improved by long-continued
    manuring with heather-sod compost.

F. ------------
    Sol sableux amélioré par une fumure continue avec des
    composts de bruyère.

D. Eschboden
    Plaggenboden
    Durch langjährige Düngung mit Heideplaggen-Kompost
    erheblich verbesserter Sandboden.

Esp. ------------
    Suelo arenoso que ha sido mejorado mediante abonamiento
    continuo con residuos de brezo.

P. ------------
    Solo arenoso que foi melhorado por contínua incorporação
    de composto de urze.

I. ------------
    Terreno sabbioso migliorato per concimazione continuata
    con composta di zolle d'eriche.

Nl. esgrond
    enkgrond
    plaggengrond
    Zandige grond die verrijkt is door langdurige bemesting
    met heideplag-compost.

S. ------------
    Sandjord som förbättrats genom riklig gödsling med kom-
    post.

S10

Eng. <u>Regosol</u>
Soil without definite genetic horizons developing from deep unconsolidated rock or soft mineral deposits.

F. <u>Regosol</u>
Sol constitué de dépôts épais de matériaux.rocheux non consolidés ou de dépôts épais de minéraux meubles. (Non utilisé en français.)

D. <u>"Regosol</u>" (m)
Boden, der sich auf unverfestigtem Gestein oder lockeren mineralischen Ablagerungen entwickelt hat.

Esp. <u>regosol</u>
Suelo constituido por rocas profundas no consolidadas o depositos minerales blandos.

P. <u>Regosolo</u>
Solo constituido por rochas profundas inconsolidadas ou por depósitos minerais brandos em que poucas ou nenhumas características pedológicas nítidas se observam.

I. <u>regosol</u>
Terreno originatiso da una.formazione profonda non consolidata o di depositi minerali incoerenti.

Nl. <u>regosol</u>
Grond bestaande uit diepe niet losse gesteenten of zachte minerale afzettingen.

S. <u>regosol-jord</u>
Jord bestående av bergartsfragment el. lösa mineralavlagringar.

Eng. Planosol

        Intrazonal soil having a sharply delineated clay pan or
hardpan arising from cementation, compaction or high clay
content; formed under forest or grassland vegetation in
mesothermal to tropical perhumid to semi-arid climates,
usually but not always with fluctuating water table.

F. Plano-sol

        Sol ayant un horizon compact, cimenté ou argileux nette-
ment marqué. (Non utilisé en français.)

D. Planosol-Boden (m)

        Intrazonaler Boden mit scharf abgesetzter Tonschicht oder
durch Zementieren verhärteter Schicht oder mit hohem Ton-
gehalt, gebildet unter Wald- oder Grasvegetation in sub-
tropischem bis tropischem perhumiden bis semiariden
Klima, gewöhnlich mit schwankendem Grundwasserspiegel.

Esp. planosol

        Suelo intrazonal con un horizonte arcilloso bien definido,
compacto y cementado. Se forma bajo vegetación de bosque
o de pradera en climas ligeramente húmedos o semiáridos
de regiones tropicales o subtropicales.

P. Planosolo

        Solo intrazonal caracterizado por um horizonte compacto
e cimentado bem definido (surraipa ou camada muito argilosa). Desenvolve-se sob vegetação florestal ou herbácea.
Geralmente, mas nem sempre, o lençol freático encontra-se
temporáriamente perto da superfície.

I. planasol (m)

        Terreno intrazonale che ha un orizzonte nettamente defi-
nito da uno strato d'argilla, oppure da uno strato duro
originato da cementazione, compressione o da alto contenuto d'argilla. È formato sotto la vegetazione di
foreste o di prati in climi mesotermici da molto umidi
tropicali a semiaridi; normalmente, ma non sempre, con
falda freatica fluttuante.

Nl. planosol

        Intrazonale grond met een scherp afgegrensde kleibank of
verharde bank, ontstaan door verkitting, verdichting of
door een hoog kleigehalte. Deze wordt onder een bos of
gras-vegetatie gevormd in sub-tropische tot tropische,
perhumiede tot semi-ariede klimaten en heeft gewoonlijk,
doch niet altijd, een wisselende grondwaterstand.

S. planosol jord

        Intrazonal jordmån med en tydligt markerad skenhälla,
orsakad av sammankittning, sammanpackning eller hög ler-
halt. Den utbildas under skogs- eller gräsvegetation i
medeltempererade till tropiska perhumida till semiarida
klimattyper, vanligen, men ej alltid, med varierande
grundvattenyta.

Section T

TERRACING, DAMMING, DRAINAGE

TERRASSES, BARRAGES, DRAINAGE

TERRAPLENES, PRESAS, AVENAMIENTO

Eng. terrace
    (1) Approximately horizontal man-made channel or bank
    for controlling run-off water.
    (2) Alluvial deposit lying on bench above the flood plain
    of a stream.

F. terrasse
    Bande de terre presque horizontale (s'applique plutôt à
    des formations naturelles — ex. terrasse fluviale — le
    qualificatif précise le sens du mot).

D. Terrasse (f)
    Annähernd horizontale Bodenfläche, mindestens an einer
    Seite abfallend.

Esp. terraza
    (1) Terraplén de tierra aproximadamente horizontal.
    (2) Franja llana de terreno sobre el nivel actual de
    inundación de un río.

P. terraço
    Faixa de terra approximadamente horizontal.

I. terrazza (f)
    Un ripiano di terra quasi orizzontale.

Nl. terras
    Vrijwel horizontaal aangelegd veld.

S. terrass
    Nästan horisontell jordbank.

Eng.   bench terrace
        Terrace with steep drop on the down-hill side.

F.   banquette
     gradin
        Surface horizontale se terminant par un talus abrupt.

D.   Bankterrasse (f)
        Terrasse mit steilem Abfall auf der Talseite.

Esp.   bancal
        Terraza con talud ompinado del lado de la vertiente.

P.   socalco
        Terraço em banco, com um talude íngreme ou vertical e
        uma parte horizontal ou suavemente inclinada, que é
        cultivada.

I.   terrazza (f)
        Un ripiano orizzontale in terra fatto dall'uomo sostenuto
        a valle da un ciglio o muro il cui paramento ha forte pen-
        denza.

Nl.   bank terras
        Terras, gelegen op een helling, dat met een steile wand
        in een lager terras overgaat.

S.   bänkterrass
        Terrass med brant släntlutning.

Eng. <u>broad-base terrace</u>
A low, wide terrace used on gentle slopes.

F. <u>terrasse à large base</u>
Terrasse basse et large utilisée sur les pentes douces.

D. <u>"Grossflächenterrasse"</u> (f)
Auf schwach geneigten Hängen verwendete niedrige breite
Terrassenform.

Esp. <u>terraza de base ancha</u>
Una terraza baja y amplia utilizada en pendientes suaves.

P. <u>terraço de base larga</u>
Um terraço baixo e largo usado em declives suaves.

I. <u>terrazza</u> (f) <u>ad onda</u> (f) <u>con il fondo</u> (m) <u>largo</u>
Un argine basso e largo che limita a monte una larga
scolina con dolce pendenza longitudinale.

Nl. <u>breed terras</u>
Een uitgestrekt terras op flauwe helling.

S. <u>bred terrass</u>
En låg, bred terrass, som används på svaga sluttningar.

Eng.   <u>step terrace</u>
        Terrace with vertical drop on the downhill side.

F.   <u>terrasse</u>
        Surface plane se terminant par un talus vertical et
        située sur le flanc d'une déclivité.

D.   <u>Stufenterrasse</u> (f)
        Terrasse mit senkrechtem Abfall auf der Talseite.

Esp.   <u>terraza de escalón</u>
        Terraza con caida vertical del lado de la bajada.

P.   <u>socalco</u>
        Terraço com muro de suporte.

I.   <u>terrazza</u> (f) <u>a gradinata</u> (f)
        Terrazza con il paramento a valle verticale.

Nl.   <u>trap terras</u>
        Terras, gelegen op een helling, dat met een loodrechte
        wand in een lager gelegen terras overgaat.

S.   <u>hyllterrass</u>
        Terrass utan dosering.

Eng. <u>drainage terrace</u>
Wide, nearly horizontal channel for removing surplus
water.

F. <u>fossé de colature</u>
<u>terrasse de colature</u>
Fossé large, presque horizontal pour évacuer l'excès
d'eau.

D. ------------
Breiter, beinahe wagrechter Kanal zur Ableitung überschüssigen Wassers.

Esp. <u>zanja de drenaje</u>
Zanja amplia, casi horizontal, para extraer el exocso
de agua.

P. <u>terraço de drenagem</u>
Canal largo e quase horizontal para remoção do excesso
de água com velocidade reduzida.

I. <u>drenaggio</u> (m) <u>a fossi</u> (m p) <u>quasi orizzontali</u>
Scoline larghe e quasi orizzontali per asportare l'acqua
in eccesso.

Nl. <u>afwateringsterras</u>
Brede strook land waarlangs de afvoer van overtollig
water kan plaats vinden.

S. <u>avrinningsterrass</u>
Bred, nästan horisontell kanal för avledning av över-
skottsvatten.

Eng.   <u>drainage</u>
  (1) Degree of removal of water from soil.
  (2) Method of removal of water from soil.
  (3) Property of soil allowing removal of water.

F.   <u>drainage</u>
  (1) Action d'éliminer l'eau en excès.
  (2) Système d'évacuation de l'eau.
  (3) Propriété que possède un sol de permettre l'écoulement de l'eau.

D.   <u>Drainage</u>
  Eigenschaft des Bodens, den Wasserabfluss zu begünstigen.
  <u>Entwässerung</u>
  Künstliche Entfernung des überschüssigen Wassers aus dem Boden, und die hierzu verwendeten technischen Einrichtungen.

Esp.   <u>drenaje</u>
  Condición del suelo drenado.

P.   <u>drenagem</u>
  Remoção da água do solo em excesso.

I.   <u>drenaggio</u> (m)
  Rimozione dell'acqua dal terreno.

Nl.   <u>afwatering</u>
  De afvoer van overtollig water uit een gebied.
  <u>ontwatering</u>
  De afvoer van overtollig water uit de grond.

S.   <u>dränering</u>
  Bortledande av vatten genom täckta ledningar.

Eng. **mole drainage**
>   Drainage provided by long tubular cavities formed by a
>   machine.

F. **drainage à la charrue taupe**
>   Système de galeries tubulaires forées dans un sol pour
>   permettre l'écoulement de l'eau; s'applique également
>   à l'assainissement du sol par ce procédé.

D. **Maulwurfs-Drainage (f)**
>   Drainage durch lange röhrenförmige Hohlräume, die mit
>   einer Maschine gemacht werden.

Esp. **drenaje topo**
>   Drenaje a través de largas cavidades tubulares formadas
>   por una máquina.

P. **drenagem feita com uma toupeira**
>   Drenagem conseguida através de cavidades tubulares aber-
>   tas por uma máquina.

I. **drenaggio (m) con aratro talpa**
>   Drenaggio per mezzo di lunghi cavi sotterranei formati
>   da una macchina.

Nl. **mol drainage**
>   Ontwatering door middel van lange, cylindervormige gan-
>   gen, die met een werktuig, de molploeg, getrokken zijn.

S. **tubulering**
>   Dränering genom långa, rörformade kanaler formade av en
>   speciell maskin (tubulator).

Eng. <u>impeded drainage</u>
Condition in which downward movement of gravitational
water is hindered.

F. <u>drainage difficile</u>
Etat de chose dans lequel le déplacement en profondeur
de l'eau est gêné.

D. <u>stauende Nässe</u> (f)
Der Zustand, bei dem die Wasserbewegung von oben nach
unten verhindert ist.

Esp. <u>drenaje restringido</u>
Condición en la cual se impide la eliminación del agua.

P. <u>má drenagem</u>
Condição do solo para à qual a remoção da água é difícil.

I. <u>scolo</u> (m) <u>imperfetto dei terreni</u>
Condizione per cui l'asportazione dell'acqua è messa in
difficoltà o minacciata.

Nl. <u>belemmerde afwatering</u>
Toestand waarbij de waterafvoer wordt belemmerd.

S. <u>försvårad genomrinning</u>
Ett tillstånd hos jorden, vid vilket avlägsnande av
vatten är försvårat.

Eng. lysimeter
      Structure enclosing mass of soil so that percolation etc.
      can be measured.

F.   lysimètre (case lysimétrique)
      Construction contenant une masse de terre permettant de
      recueillir les eaux de drainage.

D.   Lysimeter
      Behälter mit Boden, der die Messung der Auswaschung usw.
      erlaubt.

Esp. lisímetro
      Estructura que encierra una masa del suelo, construida
      en tal forma que puede medirse la percolación, etc.

P.   lisimetro
      Construção cheia de massa do solo de forma a permitir
      que a infiltração etc. possam ser medidas.

I.   lisimetro (m)
      Dispositivo che rinchiude una certa massa di terreno in
      modo tale che possano esser misurate la percolazione,
      ecc.

Nl.   lysimeter
      Een installatie, die een hoeveelheid grond bevat en die
      zo is ingericht, dat de percolatie enz. kan worden
      gemeten.

S.   lysimeter
      Anordning för mätande av genomrinning m.m. i en jord.

Eng. <u>dam</u>
      Barrier built to hold back water and raise its level.

F.   <u>barrage-réservoir</u>
      Construction destinée à accumuler l'eau.

D.   <u>Staudamm</u> (m)
      Vorrichtung für den Wasserstau.

Esp. <u>dique</u>
      Estructura para almacenar agua.

P.   <u>barragem</u>
      <u>represa</u>
      Construção para o armazenamento da água.

I.   <u>diga</u> (f)
      Struttura per invasare l'acqua.
      <u>serra</u> (f)
      <u>briglia</u> (f)
      Struttura interposta sui corsi d'acqua (torrenti) per
      ridurre la pendenza del fondo.

Nl.   <u>reservoirdam</u>, (stuwmeerdam)
      Kunstwerk voor de opstuwing en opzameling van water in
      een stuwmeer.

S.   <u>damm</u>
      <u>dammbyggnad</u>
      Konstruktion för vattenmagasinering (i ett dike eller
      vattendrag inbyggt hinder så att vattenytan höjes).

Eng. **barrage**
        Structure for raising level of water in a river.

F.   **barrage**
        Construction destinée à élever le niveau de l'eau de la
        rivière.

D.   **Staudamm** (m)
      Damm (m)
        Vorrichtung für den Wasserstau.

Esp. **presa de contención**
        Estructura para desviar el agua del río.

P.   **açude de derivação**
        Construção para desviar o curso da água do rio.

I.   **sbarramento** (m) **di derivazione** (f)
      diga (f) **di derivazione**
        Struttura per deviare le acque di un fiume.

Nl.   **stuw**
      stuwdam
        Kunstwerk voor het opstuwen en aftappen van water uit
        een rivier.

S.   **fördämning**
        Vallbyggnad som avböjer loppet av en flod till ändrad
        riktning.

Section U

IRRIGATION

IRRIGATION

RIEGO

Eng.   perennial irrigation
         Water is applied at intervals throughout the year.

F.   irrigation pérenne
         L'eau est répandue périodiquement tout au long de
         l'année.

D.   "Bewässerung (f) während des ganzen Jahres"
         In Abständen wird das ganze Jahr hindurch bewässert.

Esp.   riego permanente (perenne)
         El agua es aplicada a intérvalos durante todo el año.

P.   rega descontínua
         A água é fornecida com intervalos durante a época de
         rega.

I.   irrigazione (f) perenne
         Gli adacquamenti vengon praticati a intervalli durante
         tutto l'anno.

Nl.   periodieke bevloeiing
         Het water wordt periodiek naar behoefte aan de aanplant
         toegediend.

S.   ständig bevattning
         Vatten tillföres periodvis under hela året.

Eng. <u>basin irrigation</u>
> Water is applied to level areas surrounded by earthen
> banks for several days to permit deep penetration,
> and then flows to the next field.

F. <u>irrigation par submersion</u>
> L'eau recouvrant la terre est maintenue par de petites
> digues en terre, sur une vaste surface de terre pour
> permettre une pénétration profonde de l'eau.

D. <u>Überstauung</u> (f)
> Wasserstau über ebenen, von Dammen umgebenen Flächen,
> mehrere Tage lang, um ein tiefes Eindringen zu bewirken.

Esp. <u>riego por compartimiento</u>
<u>riego en casuela</u>
> El agua es retenida por bordes de tierra sobre una
> amplia superficie de un suelo pesado por espacio de
> varios días, para permitir una penetración profunda
> de la misma, luego se pasa al campo próximo.

P. <u>rega por submersão</u>
> A água é retida, por meio de valados, numa vasta área
> de solo compacto durante vários dias para permitir a
> profunda penetração no solo e em seguida desviada para
> o próximo campo.

I. <u>irrigazione</u> (f) <u>per sommersione</u> (f) <u>a scomparti</u> (m p) <u>grandi</u>
> L'acqua viene contenuta, per mezzo di argini di terra,
> su una larga zona di terreno pesante per alcuni giorni
> onde consentire una profonda penetrazione, e quindi viene
> fatta defluire nel campo successivo.

Nl. <u>bassin-bevochtiging</u>
> Het rivierwater wordt tijdens hoge rivierstanden op de
> oeverlanden toegelaten en daar vastgehouden tussen
> dijken. Wanneer een vak voldoende diep doordrenkt is,
> wordt het water naar een lager gelegen vak gevoerd en
> wordt het eerste vak beplant.

S. <u>överdämning</u>
> Vatten får stå över markytan en viss tid för att kunna
> tränga ned i marken innan det får flyta vidare till
> nästa fält.

Eng. basin check method
      Water flows into level areas, about 0.5 hectare in area,
      separated by low earthen banks.

F. irrigation par submersion contrôlée
      L'eau s'écoule dans des cuvettes horizontales, de 0,5 ha
      de superficie environ, séparées par des diguettes en
      terre.

D. ---
      Beriezelung ebener Flächen die etwa 0,5 ha gross und
      durch niedere Erddämme voneinander abgetrennt sind.

Esp. método de riego por compartimientos
      El agua se deja entrar en compartimientos nivelados,
      de unas 0,5 ha de superficie, separados por bordes
      bajos de tierra.

P. método de submersão em canteiros
      A água inunda canteiros nivelados com área de cerca de
      0,5 ha separados por marachas.

I. irrigazione (f) per sommersione (f) a scomparti (m p) piccoli
      L'acqua scorre in scomparti livellati di circa ha 0,5
      delimitati da piccoli argini in terra.

Nl. kombevloeiing in vlak terrein
      Het water wordt toegelaten in vrijwel horizontale vakken,
      ca 0,5 ha groot, omgeven door lage dijkjes. De bodem
      wordt geheel geïnundeerd; de methode is in het bijzonder
      geschikt voor boomgaarden.

S. överdämning efter figurindelning
      Vatten ledes till grunda bassanger med en areal av c:a
      0,5 ha, skilda från varandra genom laga jordvallar.

U4

Eng. <u>border method</u>
      Water flows over long narrow strips with slight slope
      separated by low earthen banks.

F.   <u>irrigation par calants</u>
      L'eau s'écoule sur de longues bandes de terrain
      étroites et de faible pente, séparées par des
      diguettes de terre.

D.   <u>"Berieselung eingefasster Landstreifen"</u>
      Wasser fliesst über lange, schmale Streifen, die nur
      schwach geneigt und durch niedere Erddämme voneinander
      abgetrennt sind.

Esp. <u>método de riego por corrimiento</u>
      El agua corre por sobre largas y estrechas fajas con
      una ligera pendiente, separadas por bordes bajos de
      tierra.

P.   <u>método das faixas</u>
      A água escorre em lâmina delgada sobre faixas estreitas
      e compridas de terra com pequeno declive separadas por
      camalhões.

I.   <u>irrigazione (f) a spianate (f p) o a campoletto (m)</u>
      L'acqua defluisce su una striscia limitata da arginelli,
      relativamente stretta, disposta secondo la massima pen-
      denza, che, del resto, è molto debole.

Nl.   <u>strooksgewijze overvloeiing</u>
      Het irrigatie water wordt toegediend aan de hoge rand
      van lange smalle en flauw afhellende stroken, die door
      lage dijkjes van elkaar gescheiden zijn.

S.   <u>översilning över konstgjorda terrasser</u>
      Översilning över svagt sluttande fält uppdelade i lång-
      smala tegar genom låga jordvallar.

Eng. bench border method
      Water flows over long narrow strips separated by low
      earthen banks located on cross-slope benches having a
      slight slope in the direction of strip.

F.   irrigation par calants avec banquettes
      L'eau s'écoule sur de longues bandes étroites séparées
      par des diguettes en terre situées sur des banquettes
      normales à la ligne de plus grande pente et ayant une
      légère pente dans le sens de la longueur des bandes
      (de culture).

D.   "Berieselung eingefasster Terrassen"
      Wasser fliesst über lange schmale, durch niedere Erd-
      dämme abgetrennte Streifen, die auf parallel zur
      Streifenrichtung schwach geneigten Terrassen angelegt
      sind.

Esp. método por corrimiento con terrazas
      El agua corre sobre fajas de tierra largas y estrechas
      separadas por caballones situados en bancales que
      tienen una pequeña pendiente en el sentido longitudinal
      de la faja.

P.   método de escorrimento por faixas
      A água escorre sobre faixas delgadas e compridas de
      terra separadas por camalhões localizados em socalcos
      oblíquos com pequeno declive em relação à faixa.

I.   irrigazione (f) a scorrimento (m) su piccole terrazze (f p)
      quasi a girapoggio (m)
      L'acqua defluisce sopra lunghe e strette striscie
      separate da modesti arginelli in terra, disposti su
      ripiani disposti quasi a girapoggio con dolce pen-
      denza secondo la direzione delle striscie.

Nl.   geterrasseerde strooksgewijze overvloeiing
      De door lage dijkjes begrensde stroken waarover de over-
      vloeiing plaats vindt, liggen min of meer evenwijdig aan
      de tranche en wijken slechts in zoverre daarvan af als
      nodig is om het geringe nodige verhang te verkrijgen.

S.   översilning över naturliga terrasser
      Översilning över svagt sluttande fält uppdelade genom
      laga jordvallar på naturliga upphöjningar.

U6

Eng. <u>contour-check method</u>
   Water flows into level basins having long earthen banks
   located on contours.

F. <u>irrigation par submersion contrôlée suivant courbes de niveau</u>
   L'eau s'écoule dans des cuvettes horizontales séparées
   par de longues digues en terre, parallèles aux courbes
   de niveau.

D. -----------------------
   Berieselung ebener Flächen die längs der Höhenlinien
   mit Erddämmen eingefasst sind.

Esp. <u>método del dique a nivel</u>
   El agua se dejar entrar en compartimientos nivelados,
   que tienen largos bordes de tierra, ubicados paralela-
   mente a las curvas de nivel.

P. <u>rega por submersão</u>
   A água inunda canteiros nivelados, limitados por mara-
   chas de terra.

I. <u>irrigazione</u> (f) <u>per sommersione su ripiani</u> (m p) <u>delimitati</u>
   <u>da argini</u> (m p) <u>secondo le curve</u> (f p) <u>di livello</u> (m)
   L'acqua scorre in scomparti delimitati da lunghi argi-
   nelli in terra disposti secondo le curve di livello.

Nl. <u>kombevloeiing in hellend terrein</u>
   De kommen worden in hellend terrein gevormd door dijkjes
   langs de tranches te leggen en het land in smalle stroken
   te terrasseren. Het meest bekende voorbeeld hiervan zijn
   de sawahs op Java, Bali enz.

S. <u>överdämning efter nivåkurvor</u>
   Vatten ledes till grunda bassänger skilda åt genom jord-
   vallar anlagda efter nivåkurvor.

Eng. contour-furrow method
      Water is applied by adjacent furrows 100-200 m long
      across the slope on controlled grades, usually 0.1-1%.

F.   irrigation par ruissellement
      L'eau ruisselle sur le terrain par débordement de
      rigoles de 100 à 200 m de long situées normalement
      à la pente générale du terrain, avec des pentes longi-
      tudinales régulières de 0,1 à 1 cm par mètre.

D.   "Höhenliniengrabenmethode"
      Die Bewässerung geschieht von nebeneinander quer zum
      Hang liegenden Gräben aus, 100 bis 200 m lang mit
      regelmässigem Gefäll von etwa 0,1 bis 1%.

Esp. riego por surcos en curvas de nivel
      El agua es aplicada por surcos adyacentes, de 100 a
      200 m de longitud, ubicados normalmente a la pendiente
      general del terreno, con declives regulares de 0,1 al
      1%.

P.   método das regadeiras em curvas de nível
      A água provém de regadeiras adjacentes de 100 a 200 m
      de comprimento localizadas normalmente em relação ao
      declive, de forma a obter-se gradientes de 0,1 a 1%.

I.   irrigazione (f) per infiltrazione (f) a solchi (m p) a
      girapoggio (m)
      L'acqua viene somministrata a mezzo di solchi ravvi-
      cinati lunghi m 100-200 disposti a girapoggio con una
      pendenza del fondo che va dallo 0,1% all'1%.

Nl.   instuwing met greppels in hellend terrein
      In hellend terrein kan men het verhang der greppels
      alleen klein houden (max. 1% min. 0,1%) door deze een
      weinig scheef langs de tranches te traceren en de
      lengte te beperken tot 100 a 200 m.

S.   översilning medelst drillar
      Vatten tillföres genom 100-200 m långa fåror som
      läggas tvärs över fallet med en lutning av 0,1 till 1%.

Eng.   controlled flooding
           Water flows through irrigation-ditch openings or over
           ditch banks as a sheet across fields, its distribution
           being controlled by size and site of ditch penings,
           and by spacing between ditches.

F.   irrigation par eau de crue dirigée
           L'eau se répand en nappe à travers les champs par des
           ouvertures aménagées dans les fossés d'irrigation ou en
           franchissant les banquettes de fossés. Sa distribution
           est commandée par la dimension et l'emplacement des
           ouvertures et par l'espacement entre les fossés.

D.   "geregelte Berieselung" (f)
           Wasser fliesst durch Öffnungen in den Bewässerungsgräben
           oder über Grabendämme in einem Strom quer über die
           Felder, wobei seine Verteilung durch Grösse und Lage der
           Dammöffnungen und durch die Abstände zwischen den Dämmen
           gelenkt wird.

Esp.   inundación regulada
           El agua circula a través de las aberturas de las
           canaletas de riego o por sobre los bordes de las
           mismas en forma de manto sobre el terreno, siendo su
           distribución regulada por el tamaño y ubicación de las
           aberturas y por la separación de las canaletas.

P.   rega regulada
           A água escorre de aberturas nas regadeiras ou sobre
           marachas na regadeira através do campo, sendo a sua
           distribuição controlada pelo tamanho e localização
           das aberturas, ou pelo intervalo entre as regadeiras.

I.   irrigazione (f) a scorrimento (m) regolata
           L'acqua defluisce attraverso delle bocchette practicate
           nei fossetti adacquatori o sugli argini del fossetto
           spagliandosi come un velo nel campo, a la sua distri-
           buzione viene regolata sia dalla grandezza delle boc-
           chette sia dalla loro ubicazione sia infine dall'inter-
           distanza dei fossetti adacquatori.

Nl.   beheerste overstroming
           Het water vloeit op dezelfde wijze als bij de wilde
           bevloeiing in een dunne laag over het veld, doch de
           hoeveelheid (en dus de laagdikte) wordt beheerst door
           vorm en aantal der openingen en door de afstand der
           irrigatie-sloten.

S.   översilning (reglerad)
           Reglerad tillförsel av vatten från bevattningsfåror,
           så att vattnet flyter över rännornas kant i ett tunt
           skikt ut över fältet. Vattentillförseln regleras
           genom kanthöjden på fårorna och genom deras inbördes
           avstånd.

Eng. **corrugation method**
      Land is moistened by seepage from furrows about 0.5-1.5 m
      apart, about 100-200 m in length, running across slight
      to moderate slopes.

F.   **méthode d'irrigation par infiltration**
      L'eau s'infiltre dans des bandes de terrain 0,5 à 1,5 m
      à partir de rigoles de 100 à 200 m de longueur, tracées
      de long de pentes faibles.

D.   **"Rillenbewässerung"** (f)
      Das Land wird durch den Stau von Gräben bewässert, die
      0,5 bis 1,5 m Abstand voneinander haben, 100 bis 200 m
      lang sind und quer zu schwach bis mässig geneigten
      Hängen verlaufen.

Esp. **método de riego por corrugación**
      método de los caballones o camellones
      La tierra es humedecida por el agua que escurre de
      surcos separados uno de otro por una distancia de 0,5
      a 1,5 m, y de unos 100 a 200 m de longitud, atravesando
      las pendientes suaves a moderadas.

Γ.   **método de infiltração por sulcos**
      A terra é humedecida pela infiltração da água pro-
      veniente de sulcos distanciados de 0,5 a 1,5 m e de 100
      a 200 m de comprimento com pequeno declive.

I.   **irrigazione** (f) **per infiltrazione** (f) **a solchi** (m p) **molto
      ravvicinati**
      L'adacquamento avviene per infiltrazione da solchi
      adacquatori interspaziati di m 0,5-1,5, lunghi m 100-
      200 disposti di traverso alla massima pendenza o
      secondo una dolce.

Nl.   **vorenbevloeiing**
      De bevochtiging van het land geschiedt met ondiepe grep-
      pels op afstanden van 0,5 tot 1,5 m. De greppels zijn
      100-200 m lang en worden, daar met het oog op erosie
      slechts beperkte snelheden mogen worden toegelaten,
      gelegd met slechts een geringe afwijking van de tranche-
      lijn.

S.   **bevattning genom infiltration från grunda fåror**
      Marken bevattnas genom infiltration från 100-200 m
      långa vattenfåror på 0,5-1,5 m avstånd från varandra,
      gående vinkelrätt mot sluttningen.

Eng. <u>cross-slope furrow method</u>
Water is applied by adjacent straight furrows from 75 to 300 m in length, located across the prevailing slope to reduce furrow gradient.

F. <u>méthode d'irrigation par ruissellement avec épis</u>
L'eau est répandue par des rigoles droites de 75 à 300 m de longueur, tracées obliquement par rapport à la pente générale du terrain, afin de réduire leur pente longitudinale.

D. <u>Quergrabenbewässerung</u> (f)
Die Bewässerung geschieht von aneinander angrenzenden geraden Gräben aus, die 75 bis 300 m lang und quer zur vorherrschenden Hangneigung angelegt sind um das Grabengefälle zu verringern.

Esp. <u>método del surco oblicuo a la pendiente</u>
El agua es aplicada por surcos derechos adyacentes de 75 a 300 m de longitud, situados oblicuamente a la pendiente predominante a fin de reducir el gradiente del surco.

P. <u>método de escorrimento por regadeiras oblíquas à curva de nível</u>
A água é distribuida em regos rectilíneos adjacentes de 75 a 300 m de comprimento dispostos obliquamente em relação ao declive máximo de forma a reduzir a queda.

I. <u>irrigazione</u> (f) <u>a scorrimento</u> (m) <u>con fossette</u> (f p) <u>in obliquo</u>
L'acqua viene somministrata per mezzo di adacquatrici diritte a lievissima pendenza lunghe m 75-300.

Nl. <u>greppelbevloeiing met beheerst verhang</u>
Het water wordt toegediend met behulp van opeenvolgende rechte greppels van 75 tot 300 m lengte, die onder een zodanige hoek met het terreinverhang zijn gelegd, dat het gewenste greppelverhang wordt verkregen.

S. <u>översilning</u>
Vatten tillföres genom 75-300 m långa fåror, som ligga vinkelrätt mot sluttningen för att minska fallet.

Eng. <u>flush irrigation</u>
   Water flows over nearly level soil in a single shallow
   flood.

F. <u>irrigation par ruissellement d'eau de crue</u>
   L'eau ruisselle en couche mince sur un terrain presque
   horizontal.

D. <u>Berieselung</u> (f)
   <u>Überschwemmungsbewässerung</u>
   Wasser fliesst in einem einzigen seichten Strom über
   fast ebenes Land.

Esp. <u>riego por derrame</u>
   El agua corre sobre un suelo casi llano en una sola
   lámina superficial.

P. <u>rega de lima</u>
   Aquela em que a água escorre sobre o solo quase plano,
   formando uma camada delgada.

I. <u>irrigazione</u> (f) <u>per scorrimento</u> (m)
   L'acqua scorre su un terreno quasi a livello sotto
   forma di allagamento in spessore piccolissimo.

Nl. <u>oversijpeling</u>
   Het water vloeit in een dunne laag over nagenoeg vlak
   land.

S. <u>engångsbevattning genom översilning</u>
   Vatten får flyta fram över en någorlunda jämn markyta
   under en viss kort tid (vid högvatten).

Eng.   furrow method
        Water is applied by adjacent furrows, 75-300 m long,
        having a slight slope.

F.   irrigation par infiltration
        L'eau est distribuée par un réseau de rigoles, longues
        de 75 à 300 m et présentant une pente faible.

D.   "Grabenmethode" (f)
        Bewässerung von nebeneinander liegenden schwach
        geneigten Gräben, die 75 bis 300 m lang sind.

Esp.   método por surcos
        El agua es aplicada por surcos adyacentes de 75 a 300 m
        de longitud que tienen una ligera pendiente, desde los
        cuales se infiltra en el terreno.

P.   método dos sulcos
        A água provém de sulcos adjacentes de comprimento entre
        75 e 300 m e de declive suave.

I.   irrigazione (f) per infiltrazione (f) a solchi (m p)
     distanziati
        L'acqua viene somministrata da solchi lunghi m 75-300
        aventi una dolce pendenza.

Nl.   instuwing met greppels in vlak terrein
        De bevloeiing geschiedt door een stelsel van greppels
        van 75 tot 300 m lengte. Toepassing is mogelijk in
        terreinen met gering verhang.

S.   översilning mellan drillar
        Vatten tillföres genom 75-300 m långa fåror med svagt
        fall.

Eng. <u>sprinkling irrigation</u>
       Water forced through pipes is distributed by sprinklers.

F. <u>méthode par aspersion</u>
       L'eau, s'écoulant sous pression dans les tuyaux, est
       distribuée en pluie par des appareils à dispersion.

D. <u>(künstliche) Beregnung</u> (f)
       Das Wasser wird durch Röhren gepumpt und mit Regnern
       verteilt.

Esp. <u>riego por aspersión</u>
    <u>riego de lluvia</u>
       El agua forzada a través de caños es distribuida por
       roceadores.

P. <u>rega pelo método da chuva</u>
       A água é transportada em canalização e distribuida com
       chuveiros.

I. <u>irrigazione</u> (f) <u>a pioggia</u> (f)
       L'acqua viene messa in pressione in una rete di tub-
       azioni dalla quale è distribuita per mezzo di ugelli
       irroratori.

Nl. <u>kunstmatige beregening</u>
       Het water wordt onder druk door een buisstelsel aan-
       gevoerd en over de planten verspreid door (gewoonlijk
       roterende) verstuivers.

S. <u>besprutningsmetoder</u>
       Vatten föres fram genom rörledningar och tillföres via
       spridare.

Eng.   subirrigation
            Water is applied in open ditches or tile lines until the
            water table is raised sufficiently to wet the root zone.

F.   irrigation souterraine
            Le niveau de la nappe phréatique est haussé, un plan
            d'eau temporaire est créé, où de l'eau est infiltrée à
            partir de conduits souterrains ou de fossés d'irrigation.

D.   Untergrundbewässerung (f)
            Der Grundwasserstand wird gehoben bzw. das Land durch
            Schliessung der unterirdischen Wasserabläufe oder der
            Entwässerungsgräben unter Wasser gesetzt.

Esp.   riego subterráneo
            Se eleva el nivel del agua del subsuelo o se establece
            una capa freática temporal por medio de afloraciones por
            los conductos subterráneos o acequias de riego.

P.   rega subterrânea
            O nível da toalha de água é levantado ou establece-se
            temporária toalha de água por infiltração de condutas
            subterrâneas ou de valas ou sulcos.

I.   subirrigazione (f)
            Si innalza il livello delle acque freatiche o si crea
            una falda freatica temporanaea per infiltrazione e
            capillarità tramite delle condotte sotterranee o delle
            adacquatrici.

Nl.   ondergrondse instuwing, (infiltratie)
            De bevochtiging wordt verkregen door met een buizen- of
            gangenstelsel de grondwaterstand tijdelijk te verhogen,
            dan wel tijdelijk een plaatselijke grondwaterstand te
            vormen. In enkele gevallen kan dit ook met een stelsel
            van open leidingen worden bereikt.

S.   grundvattenuppdämning
            Grundvattenytan höjes eller hålles vid en bestämd nivå
            genom infiltration från täckta ledningar eller bevatt-
            ningskanaler.

Section V

E ROSION

E ROSION

E ROSION

Eng. <u>accelerated erosion</u>
      An increase in the rate of erosion, caused by the acti-
      vities of man.

F.   <u>érosion accélérée</u>
      Entraînement relativement rapide des terres.

D.   <u>beschleunigte Erosion</u> (f)
      Die verhältnismässig rasche Abtragung von Land, das vom
      Menschen genutzt wird.

Esp. <u>erosión acelerada</u>
      Desgaste comparativamente rápido del suelo utilizado
      por el hombre.

P.   <u>erosão acelerada</u>
      Desgaste rápido da terra devido à interferência do
      homem.

I.   <u>erosione</u> (f) <u>accelerata</u>
      Il logoramento relativamente rapido della terra utiliz-
      zata dall'uomo.

Nl.   <u>versnelde erosie</u>
      Toename van de normale erosie als gevolg van (onoordeel-
      kundig) landgebruik.

S.   <u>påskyndad erosion</u>
      Rel. snabb erosion i odlade områden.

V2

Eng. gully
>   Large channel cut by running water.

F.   ravin
>   Tranchée creusée par l'eau courante.

D.   Erosionsgraben (m)
>   Durch fliessendes Wasser gebildeter Graben.

Esp. cárcava
>   Excavación abierta por el agua al correr.

P.   ravina
>   Barranco produzido pelo escoamento da água.

I.   burrone (m)
>   Incisione dovuta all'azione erosiva delle acque correnti.

Nl.   geul
>   Een geul, die is gevormd door stromend water.

S.   ravin
>   Fördjupning i terrängen bildad av rinnande vatten.

Eng.   <u>gully erosion</u>
         Erosion that cuts deep channels into land.

F.   <u>érosion en ravins</u>
        <u>ravinement</u>
         Erosion qui creuse des canaux profonds dans le sol.

D.   <u>Grabenerosion</u> (f), <u>(Tiefenerosion)</u> (f)
         Erosion, welche tiefe Gräben in das Land einfrisst.

Esp.   <u>erosión en cárcava</u>
         Erosión que causa profundos canales en el suelo.

P.   <u>erosão em ravinas</u>
         Erosão que escava profundos barrancos na terra.

I.   <u>burronamento</u> (m)
         Tipo di erosione che scava nel terreno profondi canali.

Nl.   <u>geul-erosie</u>
         Erosie, die diepe geulen in het land uitschuurt.

S.   <u>ravinbildning genom erosion</u>
         Erosion som ger upphov till stora raviner i lösa avla-
        gringar.

V4

Eng. **rill erosion**
Formation of small channels by the uneven removal of
surface soil by running water.

F. **érosion en rigoles**
Entraînement du sol superficiel, par l'eau dans de
petits canaux.

D. **Rinnenerosion** (f)
Bildung kleiner Kanäle infolge ungleichmässiger Entfernung von Oberflächenboden durch fliessendes Wasser.

Esp. **erosión en surcos**
La remoción y pérdida de suelo superficial en pequeños
canales, ocasionada por el agua.

P. **erosão em sulcos**
A remoção do solo superficial pela água, formandose
pequenos regos.

I. **erosione** (f) **per ruscellamento** (m)
L'asportazione de la superficie del suolo dovuta
all'acqua concentrata in tanti piccoli rivoli.

Nl. **geul-erosie**
Verwijdering van bovengrond door afstromend water in
kleine geultjes.

S. **rännilerosion**
Bortförande av jord genom vatten strömmande i rännilar.

Eng. <u>sheet erosion</u>
      The gradual, uniform removal of surface soil by water.

F. <u>érosion en nappe</u>
    <u>érosion par couches</u>
      Entraînement progressif et uniforme du sol superficiel
      par l'eau.

D. <u>Flächenerosion</u> (f)
      Der allmähliche gleichmässige Abtrag von Oberflächen-
      boden.

Esp. <u>erosión laminar</u>
      La remoción y pérdida gradual, uniforme de suelo super-
      ficial ocasionada por el agua.

P. <u>erosão laminar</u>
      A gradual e uniforme remoção da superfície do solo pela
      água.

I. <u>erosione</u> (f) <u>superficiale</u>
      La graduale e uniforme asportazione del terreno dovuta
      all'azione idrica e delle meteore.
    <u>calo</u> (m) <u>di denudamento</u>
      La graduale e uniforme asportazione del terreno più
      superficiale dovuta alle lavorazioni.

Nl. <u>vlakte-afspoeling</u>
      Het geleidelijk en gelijkmatig afspoelen van bovengrond
      door water.

S. <u>yterosion</u>
      En gradvis, likformig borttransport av ytjord genom
      vatten.

V6

Eng. **soil creep**
      solifluxion
          Slow movement of soil material under the force of
          gravity.

F.   **solifluxion**
          Mouvement en masse d'un sol sous forme plus ou moins
          boueuse, sous l'influence de la pesanteur.

D.   **Bodenkriechen** (n)
      Solifluction (f)
          Bewegung von Bodenmaterial unter dem Einfluss der
          Schwerkraft.

Esp. **deslizamiento del suelo**
          Movimiento descendente lento del suelo en laderas.

P.   **escorregamento**
          Movimento do material do solo devido à fôrça da gravi-
          dade.

I.   **soliflussione** (f)
          Movimento del materiale terroso sotto la forza di gra-
          vità.

Nl.   **solifluctie**
          Afglijding van grond in brei toestand onder invloed
          van de zwaartekracht.

S.   **jordflytning**
          Rörelse i vattenmättad jord, orsakad av tyngdkraft.

Eng.   land slide
        (1) Rapid movement down hill of a mass of soil, rock or
        debris.
        (2) Mass of material that has slipped down hill.

F.   glissement de terrain
        Mouvement rapide d'une masse de terre vers le bas.

D.   Erdrutsch (m)
        Schnelle Abwärtsbewegung einer grösseren Masse von Boden-
        material.

Esp.   derrumbe
        Movimiento rápido, ladera abajo, de una masa de suelo.

P.   abatimento de terra
        Movimento rápido descendente do solo.

I.   frana (f)
        franamento (m)
        Rapido movimento verso valle di una massa di terreno.

Nl.   aardstorting
        Snelle bergafwaartse beweging van een grondmassa.

S.   jordskred
        En rel. hastig rörelse nedför en sluttning av en jord-
        massa.

Eng. shifting sand
      Sand continuously moved by wind.

F. sable mobile
      Sable continuellement déplacé par le vent.

D. Flugsand (m)
      Sand, der über weite Strecken durch Wind bewegt wird.

Esp. arena movediza
      Arena movida continuamente por el viento.

P. arcia movediça
      Areia que se move por a acção do vento.

I. sabbia (f) vagante
      Sabbie che si mouvono continuamente in traslazione sotto
      la spinta del vento.

Nl. stuifzand
      Zand, dat voortdurend door de wind wordt of werd ver-
      plaatst.

S. flygsand
      Grövre vindburna sediment.

Eng.   base level of erosion
        The lowest level to which a stream can erode its bed.

F.   niveau de base de l'érosion
        Niveau stable à partir duquel remonte l'érosion de la
        rivière.

D.   Erosionsbasis
        Niedrigstes Erosionsniveau eines Flusses bezogen auf
        einen Punkt an diesen Fluss (unterhalb der Quelle).

Esp.   "nivel mínimo de erosión"
        El nivel más bajo al que un río puede erosionar su pro-
        pio lecho.

P.   nível básico de erosão
        O mais baixo nível a que um curso de água pode erosionar
        o seu leito.

I.   livello (m) base di erosione
        Livello più basso a cui è arrivata l'erosione.

Nl.   erosiebasis
        Het laagste niveau, dat een rivier door insnijding kan
        bereiken.

S.   erosionsbas
        Den vattennivå där all erosion upphör.

INDEX

red loam   R.8
Red Podzolic soil   N.7
Reddish Brown Lateritic soil R.2
Reddish Brown (steppe) soil P.10
Reddish Chestnut soil   P.12
Reddish Prairie soil   P.13
Regosol   S.10
regur   R.11
Rendzina   S.1
residual shrinkage   A.9
residual soil   S.5
rhizosphere   H.5
rill erosion   V.4

talus   J.11
Terra Rossa   R.6
terrace   T.1
texture   B.1
till   J.7
tilth   G.6
tirr   M.17
tirs   R.12
top soil   G.9
trace element   D.26
transitional moor   M.2
transitional soil   S.6
transported soil   S.4
tundra   M.6
tundra soil   M.7
truncated   H.11
type (soil)   L.10

S value   D.20
saline soil   Q.1
sand   B.3
second bottom   J.18
secondary mineral   K.3
secondary soil   S.4
sedimentation analysis   B.14
series (soil)   L.11
sheet erosion   V.5
shifting sand   V.8
siallitic   D.5
sierozem   P.14
silica-sesquioxide ratio   D.3
silt   B.8
silt and clay   B.9
single-grain structure   B.27
skeletal soil   S.3
smonitza   P.7
soil creep   V.6
soil-moisture tension   C.20
solifluxion   V.6
Solod (Soloth)   Q.4
Solonchak   Q.2
Solonetz   Q.3
solum   L.1
sprinkling irrigation   U.13
"stable humus"   E.15
step terrace   T.4
sticky point   C.8
strip cropping   G.2
structure   B.17
structure index   B.18
subirrigation   U.14
subsoil   G.10
suction   C.20
summation curve   B.15
swamp   M.8
szik soil   Q.5

ultimate particle   B.26
"unstable humus"   E.16
upper plastic limit   C.9

water table   C.23
waterlogging   C.24
watershed   J.16
wet meadow soil   O.1
Wiesenboden   O.1
wilting percentage (point) C.11

Yellow Podzolic soils   N.8
yellowish brown lateritic
   soil   R.3
younger peat   M.14

zonal soil   L.5

406

----

maduro   H.7
mantillo   E.3
marga   J.2
método de los caballones o
   camellones   U.9
método de riego por
   compartimientos   U.3
método de riego por
   corrimiento   U.4
método de riego por
   corrugación   U.9
método del dique a nivel   U.6
método del surco oblicuo a la
   pendiente   U.10
método por corrimiento con
   terrazas   U.5
método por surcos   U.12
micorriza   F.4
micro-elemento   D.26
mineral ferruginoso
   limonítico   I.26
mineral primario   K.2
mineral secundario   K.3
minerales de arcilla   K.1
mineralización   F.5
monolito de suelo   I.2
morfología   H.6
mullido   G.4
muñequita   I.29

pantano   M.8
partícula elemental   B.26
pavimento desértico   J.12
"pedalfer"   L.3
pedernal   J.4
"pedocal"   L.4
pedogénesis   H.2
pedósfera   H.1
películas de agua   C.14
penillanura   J.14
pérdida por calcinación   D.1
perdigones   I.27
perfil de suelo   I.1
permeabilidad   A.5
pF   C.18
piedra ferruginosa   I.25
piso de arado   G.8
planosol   S.11
plantas indicadoras   F.2
plástico   A.4
podsol hidromórfico   N.6
porcentaje de 15 atmósferas C.7
porcentaje de saturación   D.19
porosidad del suelo   A.6
potencial capilar   C.17
presa de contención   T.11
pseudo micelio   I.30
punto de adherencia   C.8
punto lento capilar   C.12

"nazzaz"   I.23
necesidad de cal   G.14
nitrificación   F.6
"nivel mínimo de erosión"   V.9
nutrimento   D.22

oligoelemento   D.26
orterde   I.21

regosol   S.10
regur   R.11
relación carbono-nitrógeno   D.2
relación sílice sesquióxidos D.3
requerimiento de abonos   G.12
reserva mineral   D.23
ribera alta   J.18
riego de lluvia   U.13
riego en casuela   U.2
riego permanente (perenne) U.1
riego por aspersión   U.13
riego por compartimiento   U.2
riego por derrame   U.11
riego por surcos en curvas de
   nivel   U.7
riego subterráneo   U.14
rizosfera   H.5
roca madre   H.3, H.4

419

420

428

431

432

435

436

438

SOME FAO PUBLICATIONS OF INTEREST TO SOIL SCIENTISTS

Using Salty Land
Agricultural Study No. 3 by H. Greene
1948, 2nd printing 1953. iii+51 pp., charts.
In English and French. $0.50 or 2s.6d.

Soil Conservation: An International Study
Agricultural Study No. 4
1948, 2nd printing 1952. viii+189 pp., illustrations, charts.
In English, French and Spanish. $2.00 or 10s.

Soil Surveys for Land Development
Agricultural Study No. 20
1953. xii+110 pp., illustrations, maps.
In English. French and Spanish editions in preparation. $1.00 or 5s.

Water Laws in the United States of America
Development Paper No. 2 by M.B. Williams
1950. iii+161 pp.
In English. $1.00 or 5s.

Water Laws in Italy
Development Paper No. 22 by D.A. Caponera
1953. iii+28 pp.
In English. $0.25 or 1s.3d.

Water Laws in Moslem Countries
Development Paper No. 43 by D.A. Caponera
1954. iv+202 pp.
In English. $2.00 or 10s.

Report of the Meeting on Fertilizer Production, Distribution and Utilization in Latin America
Development Paper No. 36
1953. iv+52 pp.
In English and Spanish. $0.50 or 2s.6d.

Land Utilization in Tropical Areas
Development Paper No. 17, being a report of an FAO Regional Meeting held at Nuwara Eliya, Ceylon, September 1951.
1952. v+10 pp.
In English, French and Spanish. $0.25 or 1s.3d.

Some Aspects of Surface Water Development in Arid Regions
Development Paper No. 21 by A. de Vajda
1952, v+45 pp.
In English and French. $0.50 or 2s.6d.

The Efficient Use of Fertilizers
Agricultural Study No. 9, by V. Ignatieff
1949. 182 pp., illustrations, maps.
In English, French and Spanish. The English edition is published by Leonard Hill Ltd., London. $2.00 or 10s.

SALES AGENTS FOR FAO PUBLICATIONS

ARGENTINA: Editorial Sudamericana, S. A., Alsina 500, Buenos Aires.
AUSTRALIA: H. A. Goddard Pty. Ltd., 255ª George Street, Sydney.
AUSTRIA: Wilhelm Frick Verlag, Graben 27, Vienna 1.
BELGIUM: Agence et Messageries de la Presse, 14-22 rue du Persil, Brussels.
BRAZIL: Livraria Agir, rua Mexico, 98-B, Rio de Janeiro.
BURMA: (Wholesale) Orient Longmans Ltd., 17 Chittaranjan Avenue, Calcutta 13, India
CANADA: The Ryerson Press, 299 Queen Street West, Toronto 2, Ontario; Periodica, 5112 Av. Papineau, Montreal, 34.
CEYLON: (Wholesale) Orient Longmans Ltd., 17 Chittaranjan Avenue, Calcutta 13, India.
CHILE: Sala y Vila Ltda., Bandera 140-F, Santiago.
COLOMBIA: "Agricultura Tropical", Carrera 13, No. 13-17, Bogotá.
COSTA RICA: Trejos Hermanos, Apartado 1313, San José.
CUBA: René de Smedt, La Casa Belga, O'Reilly 455, Havana.
CYPRUS: Marcos E. Constantinides, P.O. Box 473, Nicosia.
DENMARK: Ejnar Munksgaard, Norregade 6, Copenhagen K.
ECUADOR: "La Hacienda", Malecón 710-711 y Roca, Guayaquil.
EGYPT: Librairie de la Renaissance d'Egypte, 9 Sh. Adly Pasha, Cairo.
EL SALVADOR: Manuel Navas y Cia., 1ª Avenida Sur 35, San Salvador.
FINLAND: Akateeminen Kirjakauppa, 2 Keskuskatu, Helsinki.
FRANCE: Les Editions A. Pedone, 13 rue Soufflot, Paris 5e.
GERMANY: Paul Parey, Lindenstr. 44-47, Berlin SW 68.
GREECE: "Eleftheroudakis", Place de la Constitution, Athens.
GUATEMALA: Goubaud y Cia. Ltda., 5ª Avenida Sur No. 28, Guatemala.
HAITI: Max Bouchereau, Librairie "A la Caravelle", Boîte postale IIIB, Port-au-Prince.
ICELAND: Halldor Jonsson, Mjostraeti 2, Reykjavik. Jonsson and Juliusson, Garoastraeti 2, Reykjavik.
INDIA: Orient Longmans Ltd., 17, Chittaranjan Avenue, Calcutta 13; Nicol Road, Ballard Estate, Bombay 1; 36-A Mount Road, Madras 2; 17/60 Sanyasiraju Street, Gandhinagar, Vijayawada 2; Kanson House, Delhi-Ajmeri Gate Scheme, New Delhi; Retail Agent: The Oxford Book and Stationery Co., Scindia House, New Delhi; 17 Park Street, Calcutta.
IRELAND: The Controller, Stationery Office, Dublin.
ISRAEL: Blumstein's Bookstores Ltd., P. O. Box 4154, Tel Aviv.
ITALY: Libreria Internazionale Ulrico Hoepli, Galleria Piazza Colonna, Rome. Libreria Internazionale Dr. Romano Romani, via Meravigli 16, Milan.
JAPAN: Maruzen Company Ltd., Tori-Nichome 6, Nihonbashi, Tokyo.
LEBANON: Librairie Universelle, Avenue des Français, Beirut.
MEXICO: Manuel Gómez Pezuela e Hijo, Donceles 12, Mexico, D. F.
NETHERLANDS: N. V. Martinus Nijhoff, Lange Voorhout 9, The Hague.
NEW ZEALAND: Whitcombe & Tombs Ltd., Auckland, Wellington, Hamilton, Christchurch, Dunedin, Invercargill, Timaru.
NORWAY: Johan Grundt Tanum Forlag, Kr. Augustsgt. 7ª, Oslo.
PAKISTAN: East: Farcos' Publications, 2 Inglis Road, P. O. Box 13, Ramna, Dacca; West: Ferozsons, 60 The Mall, Lahore.
PERU: Libreria Internacional del Perú, S. A., Casilla 1417, Lima.
PHILIPPINES. D. P. Pérez Company, 169 Riverside, San Juan, Rizal.
PORTUGAL: Livraria Bertrand, S. A. R. L., Rua Garrett 73-75, Lisbon.
SPAIN: Aguilar S.A. Ediciones, Juan Bravo 38, Madrid; José Bosch Librero, Ronda Universidad 11, Barcelona.
SWEDEN: C. E. Fritze, Fredsgatan 2, Stockholm 16; Gumperts AB, Göteborg; Henrik Lindstahls Bokhandel, Odengatan 22, Stockholm.
SWITZERLAND: Librairie Payot, S. A., Lausanne and Geneva; Hans Raunhardt, Kirchgasse 17, Zurich 1.
SYRIA: Librairie Universelle, Avenue Fouad 1er, Boîte postale 336, Damascus.
TAIWAN: The World Book Company Ltd., 99 Chungking South Road, Section I, Taipei.
THAILAND: Requests for FAO publications should be addressed to: FAO Regional Office for Asia and the Far East, Maliwan Mansion, Bangkok.
TURKEY: Librairie Hachette, 469 Istiklal Caddesi, Beyoglu, Istanbul.
UNION OF SOUTH AFRICA: Van Schaik's Book Store, Pty. Ltd., P. O. Box 724, Pretoria.
UNITED KINGDOM: H. M. Stationery Office, P. O. Box 569, London S.E.1.
UNITED STATES OF AMERICA: Columbia University Press, International Documents Service, 2960 Broadway, New York 27, N. Y.
URUGUAY: Héctor d'Elia, Oficina de Representación de Editoriales, 18 de julio 1333, Montevideo.
VENEZUELA: Suma S. A., Sabana Grande 102, "El Recreo", Caracas.
YUGOSLAVIA: Drzavno Preduzece, Jugoslovenska Knjiga, Belgrade.
Requests from countries where sales agents have not yet been appointed may be sent to: FAO Documents Sales Service, Food and Agriculture Organization of the United Nations, Viale delle Terme di Caracalla, Rome, Italy.

FAO publications are priced in U. S. dollars and pounds sterling. Payment to FAO sales agents may be made in local currencies.